Essential Oils for
HORSES

Essential Oils for
HORSES

A Source Book for Practitioners and Owners

CAROLE FAITH

MICHT, IIHHT, BABTAC
Photography by Jon Stone

J. A. ALLEN

ISBN 978-0-85131-846-2

J.A. Allen
Clerkenwell House
Clerkenwell Green
London EC1R 0HT

J.A. Allen is an imprint of Robert Hale Limited

www.halebooks.com

British Library Cataloguing in Publication Data
A catalogue record for this book is available from the British Library

Design by Judy Linard
Photographs by Jon Stone
Edited by Lesley Young
Printed in Singapore by Kyodo Printing Co (S'pore) Pte Limited

Contents

A Note for USA Readers
Please note that bracketed $ amounts shown throughout the book are not true conversions but convey price differences between UK and USA.

Conversion Chart for the USA

2.5 ml	=	$\frac{1}{2}$ tsp	50 ml = $\frac{1}{4}$ cup
5 ml	=	1 tsp	70 ml = 5 tbsp
10 ml	=	2 tsp	100 ml = $\frac{1}{2}$ cup
15 ml	=	1 tbsp	225 ml = 1 cup
20 ml	=	4 tsp	500 ml = $2\frac{1}{4}$ cups (about 1 pint)
30 ml	=	2 tbsp	1 liter = $4\frac{1}{2}$ cups (a little over 1 quart)
40 ml	=	3 tbsp	

Author's Note

'What do you do?' It is a simple, but standard question of social gatherings the world over. We are very often defined by what it is we do. I say that I am an essential oil therapist. The reply is usually a rather disinterested 'Oh yes'. I then say that I work on horses. There is always a momentary silence and then the questions start, and always the fact that I use essential oils on horses is greeted with puzzled incredulity. I must surely be joking! But why the world at large should find such a thing so unusual is something that *I* find puzzling.

It is hard to pinpoint the defining moment that made me decide to work on horses with these very special liquids. What I can say is that it was an ordinary day containing an *extraordinary* decision and one that was to lead to a whole new way of thinking and believing. In many ways I hope that this book and all it contains will go some way towards doing the same for anyone who reads it.

One of the questions I am most often asked is why I call myself an 'essential oil therapist' as opposed to an 'aromatherapist'. The answer is simple enough and yet a purely personal viewpoint. It is to do with respect. It is a fact of human nature that we pigeon hole people, either deliberately or subconsciously and then, having categorised them, judge them on that. Aromatherapy conjures up images that have no relevance to anyone dealing with horses. I also feel that I am more than an aroma-specialist too, which is what the name can sometimes suggest. Aromatherapy does seem to be inextricably linked with the human element and if that is a defining feature, who am I to argue the point? If the term essential oil therapist will gain more respect for the work I do than the word aromatherapist, then, purely from a personal viewpoint, I will use it.

That I came to use essential oils on horses was a complete accident. If you are faced with a situation that offers no discernible answers, it is, I believe, quite possible within the human psyche to seek an alternative.

Ergo, when faced with a mare – 'a lady of a certain age' shall we say –

who was tired in mind and body, and with whom all things had been tried, with little or no success, then to take up a chance-read article on oil of Rosemary, and to see the results of the use of that oil – it is not difficult to see why it is that I am where I am today, doing what it is I do. It could be said that two drops of Rosemary oil changed my life. It certainly began a few changes in the life of my horse.

I was fortunate enough to find someone to teach me about essential oils who was open minded and understood that we have barely uncovered the tip of the iceberg that is essential oils. This lady was a believer in reiki, and in the spirit of all things, and with her vast knowledge of oils, I could not have wished for a better tutor. I can only thank her for the way she embraced my desire to use them on horses with such open-minded acceptance. I think we all learnt a great deal from the experience.

Is it any different to using essential oils on humans? I am always asked this question. The answer is yes and no. No, in as much as a respiratory system is a system that effects breathing, whether in animal or human, and an injured muscle is an injured muscle no matter what skeletal frame it might be attached to. Then yes, because horses are completely different to human beings in so many ways. For one thing, they are rarely blighted by scepticism (except perhaps for my 'lady of a certain age' who shows very healthy signs of it) and they are able to recognise a need, seek its remedy and embrace it. It is a human's scepticism and constant need for analysis that very often provide the stumbling block to them regaining balance and therefore maintaining health. Horses are natural communicators. Their very survival as a species depended upon this, and, to a large extent, still does. Horses who do not communicate with humans do not do so because they have, without doubt, at some point in their lives, been let down by a human. So many times I have seen a horse trying to communicate, only for that communication to be either misread or, worse still, not heard at all by the human the horse is trying to connect to. The old saying that a bad horseman cannot hear his horse scream and yet a good one can hear his horse whisper is one I truly believe in.

I hope that reading this book will lead you to be able to hear your own horse whisper to you, to help you communicate with it far more deeply than you perhaps have done to date, and for this to help forge a bond between you that is brought about by understanding your horse's needs and being able to furnish them.

The role of the equine essential oil therapist is still obviously a new one. It is very often viewed with suspicion and dislike, by horse owners and vets alike. It will take time and patience to bring this role to a level where it is understood and accepted. It is those owners and vets who do embrace it, who use the two facets of veterinary care – conventional and comple-mentary – in harmony with each other, who are the real pioneers and who really need acknowledgement, for, without them, there is no future for this form of complementary therapy and that would be a true loss to both the equine and the veterinary worlds.

PURCHASING ESSENTIAL OILS

Always ask for the oil you require by name. For instance, if you require Peppermint USA, make sure you ask for it specifically. This is because there are several different oils, produced in different countries under different growing conditions, all defined as 'peppermint'. When you find an oil you like, make a note of the name, so that you can order the same oil next time.

Shop around for your oils. Ask a few companies to quote for the specific oil you require. One company may be very much more expensive than another. Beware the 'bargain' price oils. There is no such thing as a bargain price oil – especially when dealing with oils such as Jasmine, Rose and the Ylang Ylang distillations. These are expensive oils. If the average price is, say, £10 ($8) and you are able to pick up an oil in the same quantity for, say, £2.50 ($2) – then don't! The chances are the oil has been stretched with another oil, or let down in some way and this will have altered its delicate balance and therapeutic property. You get what you pay for in the essential oil world! That is not to say if a Jasmine oil is being sold at £10 ($8) by one company and £8 ($6) at another that you should not go for the £8 ($6) oil – I am more concerned with oils that appear to be a fraction of the normal price, not normal market fluctuation.

The price of an oil may also be affected by the quality of the harvest. For example, following a very wet spring and a summer without much sun, Lavender prices may be much more expensive than the previous season. Market forces do affect the prices of oils, so if an oil suddenly seems expensive, ask why! If you do not receive a satisfactory answer check the prices elsewhere.

If you bear these points in mind you should not have any trouble when it comes to purchasing your oils.

CHAPTER 1

The History of Essential Oils

It is always extremely easy to bypass some sections of a book in order to reach the parts that are deemed to matter or be of interest. However, to miss the chapter on the history of these substances would be doing oneself a great disservice. The history itself is fascinating. It gives an insight into the age of these substances, giving the lie to the belief that they are a 'new-fangled' passing fancy that will be forgotten given a year or two. History is yesterday, without which we cannot have today. History is what makes us what and who we are. It is no different where these precious substances are concerned. Understand something of their history and that will give you, the reader, greater access to an understanding of what they stand for today, and, through that, acknowledgement of the best way to utilise these ancient remedies for your own use in today's environment.

Firstly, we should ask ourselves – what is an essential oil? Literally, it is a highly concentrated, volatile substance obtained from various parts of an aromatic plant. The term 'volatile' refers to the oil evaporating on contact with air. An essential oil is also highly aromatic – it is the smell of it that we first register. The oil is a highly concentrated substance – up to 100 times more so after extraction than when still part of the plant. An essential oil is a very complex chemical compound; there are sometimes over 200 chemical constituents in one oil. Essential oils are mostly liquid at room temperature, although there are a few that are of a thicker consistency (Benzoin is one of these). An essential oil, on the whole, is a mostly colourless to pale yellow liquid. Obviously there are exceptions to this, as some are green-hued or even brown. As you can see already, it is not just an innocuous liquid after all.

The second question we should ask is – what is an essential oil used for?

It could be said that an essential oil is merely a pleasant-smelling cosmetic substance. That would, however, be akin to calling Concorde 'just a mode of transport'. Whilst it most definitely is a pleasant-smelling substance used by the cosmetic trade, it is much more accurate to say that it is a substance used to bring about a state of synergy within the body, the substance being able to promote and maintain physiological balance and health. Ergo, it can be used for almost anything. An essential oil also has psychological effects that are far reaching. There are oils that promote spiritual healing within us and which are somehow able to touch our very soul – our own essence responding to that of another. Horses are sensitive spiritual beings and their responses to these oils are quite remarkable to observe.

The Early History of Essential Oils

To attempt to date the first use of essential oils is virtually impossible. During the early days of the human race there was no method of documenting life, although it has to be supposed, on the basis of later research, that early people did as their later counterparts and used whatever resources they had to hand. Whatever grew was used. However, there are records in one form or another which depict the use of plants in a medicinal capacity many thousands of years before Christ. These records are mostly in the form of hieroglyphics rather than written documentation. This knowledge was learnt, practised and passed down by word of mouth. Practitioners were not trained as they are today, but, rather, were designated by circumstantial accident, in that one person became known for their knowledge of plants and their uses. Those people would have been sought out by others and so, by deed and word of mouth, information was learned and passed on. Eventually, as time passed, medicine men and women became common in tribes – an early form of general practitioner with 'surgeries' much like those we have today. Suspicion is not a new concept – even then the healing powers of the oils could arouse fears and create tensions in those who did not understand the use of the plants, and mutterings about witchcraft were not unknown.

Thousands of years ago resources would have been limited to what was locally available to wherever a tribe may have settled in what we know today as the Eastern European states, China or Western Europe. There were no drug companies inventing antibiotics for use against infection. There were only the plants that grew around them and the people who had discovered how to use them. Historical documents have indicated that, the world over, ancient peoples were discovering and using plant-based materials to combat illness, disease and maladies that affected the mind.

Some of the earliest known recordings of the use of plant materials were made by the Egyptians, an intelligent race of people who used plants extensively in both religious ceremonies and general health capacities. These uses are little changed today. One well-known and well-documented ancient remedy was Kyphi. This was a blend of 16 different aromatic plant substances, creating a perfume which could be used on the body or in religious ceremonies. It is said to have purified the air and therefore prevented the spread of disease – the antiseptic elements of the preparation coming to the fore. Many other preparations were based on the compound of Kyphi. These were used to combat insomnia and lack of concentration and for soothing respiratory complaints. They were also crudely 'vaporised' to purify and scent the air. Some of the oils in use at that time would have been Myrrh (which Roman soldiers took into battle as a wound dressing) and Frankincense (which grows in northern and eastern Africa and throughout the Arab countries) – oils still used extensively today.

The offerings of Myrrh and Frankincense to Jesus by the wise men were not idle gifts for a new born baby. They had a purpose. Both Myrrh and Frankincense are healing oils, used on wounds and for respiratory ailments, but they also contain a great spiritual depth. They would have been received and accepted as gifts of importance and great substance, and unaffordable by most ordinary people. Frankincense is also known as the 'grief' oil. It lifts the spirits and distances feelings of loss, comforting the inner soul. I still use it in that capacity today. Mary may well have found such an oil a great comfort in the days after Jesus was crucified. No doubt Myrrh would also have been used on the wounds Jesus suffered during his crucifixion. What is so remarkable is that two thousand years later we are still using the same oils for the same ailments.

The Roman Empire was also responsible for the spread of learning where herbs and plants were concerned. The Romans believed in education and many of their servants and citizens were trained to be doctors, teachers, philosophers and physicians. Within these spheres of education herbalism would have found its niche and many of the educated people would have studied this subject and utilised their findings. The growth of the Roman Empire also increased levels of travel and the

Romans became a mobile civilisation, which, in part, was one of the causes of its later fragmentation – it is hard to police a mobile population. As travel broadened and contact with other nations was established, so much more was learnt from other civilisations about the medicinal use of plants. A Roman doctor – Discorides – spent years compiling a detailed herbal volume known as *De Materia Medica* and it was from this that many remedies and their effects upon the human body were learnt, passed on and enlarged upon still further. It was also during the time of the Romans that doctors and physicians began to experiment, to prepare and use lotions, creams and ointments. The knowledge of the Romans spread throughout the world where it was incorporated with the use of indigenous plants and local remedies, some of which still exist today.

The fall of the Roman Empire brought about an exodus of educated people who, with their work and writings, fled to other countries and safety. One place to accumulate a mass of human knowledge was the port of Constantinople where influences from Greek, Egyptian and Arabic cultures combined in a whirlpool of learning and knowledge, much of which still exists in one form or another today.

Sea trade with the Middle East was also a potent force in the spread of herbal remedies. Along with silks and other commodities came plants, extracts and the knowledge of how to use them to human advantage. Plant remedies were valuable goods and would have been worth a lot of money to those selling or bartering them. The extraction methods of these substances would have been crude and it was an Arab who refined the extraction method of distillation. Avicenna (Arabic name Ali Ibn Sina) studied the use of plants and recorded the therapeutic effects of each plant in minute detail. The result was a definitive work on herbalism, which eventually reached Western culture.

Whilst it is known that plants were used in Europe during the Middle Ages, their use and documentation is very scarce. However, with the Crusades came a wider use of plants which had been brought back from the Holy Land and Arabia. Evidence shows that, in Europe, Lavender, Rosemary, Sage and Thyme were used, whilst the return of knights and other travellers, bringing new plants, documentation and more sophisticated methods of extraction, allowed a better understanding and use of these plants, together with new species which were now encouraged to grow in foreign countries.

Each century has brought forth its own scholar in the work of herbalism – for instance, in the 1500s the first English-language herbalist manuscript was written by William Turner. He was followed in the 1600s by Culpepper – a name most of us already know. Culpepper devoted his life to herbalism and wrote an extensive volume called *The Complete Herbal* from which many of our modern-day herbal remedies are derived.

Herbalism then took a backward step for many years as the educational and industrial revolutions took a hold and spread their effects. Synthetic medicines began to be produced and medicinal remedies moved towards the conventional source that we know today. The ease of administering these new, synthetic drugs and the fact that they could be mass produced caused a decline in the use of herbs, plants and flowers as a remedy for illness.

The Modern History of Essential Oils

A renaissance in the use of oils began with an accident. Rene Gattefosse, a Frenchman whose family owned a large perfumery, burnt his hands badly. Without thinking he plunged his hands into the nearest liquid, which happened to be a vat of Lavender oil. The oil effected a healing process that was more rapid than anything hitherto documented, repelled infection and minimised the scarring almost to nothing at all. Gattefosse had rediscovered the use of plant materials – in this case essential oils – and their therapeutic uses.

Until that time the liquid substances obtained from plant material had been known merely as herbal remedies. It was due to his connection with the perfume trade that Gattefosse invented the term *'aromatherapie'*, meaning literally 'healing smells'. It was also Gattefosse who referred to the liquids extracted from the plants as 'oils', due mainly to the fact that they separated in water.

It was in these later years, when pharmaceutical advances meant that substances could be properly analysed, that the true complex chemical nature of plants was discovered. Each genus of plant had a different chromotology and each variety of a plant a different one still, the reading depending on where the plant had been grown, at what altitude and in what soil and climate. The chemical constituents discovered in the plants were isolated, but did not have the same therapeutic effect in isolation nor in synthetic production as they did before extraction. The same holds true today – that an entire oil is stronger than the sum of its parts.

The use of essential oils in its present guise was brought to Britain by Marguerite Maury who had studied the works of another Frenchman, Dr Jean Valnet. Using the oils within the framework of her beautician work,

Madame Maury first began to employ them in a synergistic manner. In doing this, she assessed the characteristics of her clients – gender, age, temperament, ailment – and matched them accordingly with suitable preparations. It was the true holistic (treating something as a whole) application of essential oils, and understanding that where one person may respond to Lavender, another, with the same ailment but with different characteristics, would not. It is in this aspect – synergy – that the secret of using essential oils lies, and I will return to this in a later chapter.

Today, there are many essential oil therapists throughout the world who also pioneer new boundaries, such as Chrissie Wildwood, Sal Battaglia, Jan Kusmirek and, of course, Robert Tisserand. These are the people who will be tomorrow's history; names that will be passed down through the annals of time.

In all of this information on the history of essential oils, there is little or no reference to their use on horses. So where would a history of these oils bear relevance in a book dedicated to their application on horses? The relevance is simply that you should always understand the nature of the beast you are dealing with. Approaching a horse with a bottle of Lavender oil is a pointless exercise if you do not understand the substance. Secondly, historically, horses were wild animals and not the domesticated creatures they mostly are today. They were not kept stabled and given short feed two or three times a day, a vet was not on hand to be called out whenever the horse showed signs of being unwell. Horses had only themselves to rely on for their survival. They roamed the plains foraging for food and the plants they needed to stay healthy. Undoubtedly, ancient medicine men and doctors would have applied the same remedies to an animal as to a human if the survival of that animal was important to the human. I have heard many stories about domesticated horses who are set free in a paddock containing an organic selection of free-growing herbs and grasses, and how they browse through the different plants, eating only those that they feel they need, leaving the other plants untouched. This aspect will be covered more extensively in another chapter.

If you have reached this far, you may well wonder what all this history has to do with horses. The answer would be 'everything and nothing'. As I mentioned earlier, to use something to the best of its capacity, you should understand it yourself. It is in the understanding of any one particular element that its true success lies. If nothing was known about these oils, they would not be used to the extent that they are and with the levels of success they enjoy – *except* by horses, who would forage for the right plant instinctively.

Reading this chapter on the history of the oils will help you, the user, to understand that this is not a new remedy at all, but an ancient art with proven results. Horses and plants go together like a hand in a glove. *Horses* understand them, *horses* know that they will bring about a balance within their body systems; instinct tells them so. *Horses* do not need to analyse or rationalise what is, to them, an essential fact.

These ancient remedies, handed down through history, do work. The day may come when we can no longer rely on conventional medicines and so long as there is plant life, there is hope for the human race and its survival. This is a fact that the intelligent and spiritually minded equine quadruped is only too aware of.

CHAPTER 2

Why Use Essential Oils on Horses?

Why indeed? Why not use over the counter remedies bought at tack shops and saddlery outlets? Why not use the veterinary surgery to obtain the things you need? There is no reason at all why you should not. In life, however, there are choices, and while we humans are making a more significant turn towards the holistic methods of looking after ourselves, the same could also be said of our care towards animals. We have reached the stage where mainstream medical practices are now part and parcel of our lives, and without them it would be like returning to the dark ages. However, many of these mainstream practices have toxic side-effects. For example, the effects of anaesthetic on our bodies are well known, especially for the very young and the very elderly. There is, therefore, a place for the use of more natural ingredients, not to replace mainstream medicines but to complement and enhance them. We now have the choice, and it is a truly significant one, of taking the best of both worlds and utilising this to our benefit. On the one hand, operations are a necessity at times, and so, therefore, is the use of anaesthetics. The difference now is that we are able to use natural ingredients to offset the not always satisfactory side-effects of chemical drug ingestion.

Complementary therapies have been enjoying a boom in the last few years. It is a growth industry with a vast turnover worth millions – and not always to the practitioners I might add. The word 'new-fangled' is often bandied about by those who do not wish to see the better side of complementary therapy. Fangled? It might well be in some cases. New? No, not at all. Plants and their extracts have been used for thousands of years all over the world. 'Re-emergence' is a better term.

Where humans are concerned this re-emergence has been steadily growing over the last decade. Where animals are concerned it is, in the main, a new thing altogether. Whilst some enlightened animal owners have used natural remedies on their animals for years, the plain fact is that in most quarters complementary therapy on animals is viewed with a deep scepticism and in some cases outright derision.

When I am asked what it is I do for a living, or if I am asked how I dealt with a certain situation and the mention of essential oil usage comes up, I can be greeted with a whole range of reactions from downright incredulity to pure out and out scepticism and often dismissal, but very occasionally a light of interest will spark in someone and that will lead yet another person down the enlightened pathway of choice. These people are, however, quite rare! Even those whose horses I have helped, and in which cases the oils have shown marvellous results, sometimes almost instantaneously, refuse to believe that the oils have in any way played a part in the animal's well-being. At the end of the day it comes down to the plain fact you either believe or you do not.

Horses are forage animals and used to looking for plants that will assist the regulation of their body systems. The instinct to find the particular plant that will ease discomfort or cure feelings of ill health, has been finely honed over centuries of evolvement. To horses, and, indeed, most wild animals, this need and the ability to recognise what plants will assist them is inherent in their very make-up. It is something they know without having to think consciously about it. The aroma of an oil which is the very essence of a plant is seen as a recognisable source by equines. They instinctively know what oils to inhale and when they have had enough of them or if they need more. They are very adept at telling you they have had enough of one oil but need another. They know how much they need. When their need is sated they simply refuse to have anything more to do with the oil at all. This is such a basic instinct within them that how it can be doubted remains a mystery to me.

With so many complementary therapies now flooding the market – why choose essential oils over any other complementary discipline?

A point to bear in mind with essential oils is their compatibility with most of the other complementary therapies. In that they are unusual. How many other disciplines are compatible with so many others?

In most of the touching therapies – Tellington, sports massage, shiatsu, pressure point therapy, acupuncture – essential oils can very easily be used in conjunction with their practice.

They are, however, not a panacea for all ills. They are not miracle cures that set themselves above all others. They do not suit every horse (or person) and, indeed, some horses prefer the Bach Flower Remedies to essential oils.

The reason they are worth using, worth keeping around the yard and home, is their versatility. They are almost chameleon-like in their therapeutic properties and, whilst dealing with the presenting problem, will very often combat something else that is entirely different at the same time.

I have been asked on many occasions why these substances are called 'oils' when in fact some of them do not resemble oil at all. The term 'oil' is applied to any greasy substance that is liquid at room temperature and is insoluble in water. These substances are the very essence of the plant, hence the term 'essential'. Essential oil is therefore more of a generic term that adequately covers each substance in a way that most people can understand.

The drawback with using essential oils for horses would seem to be the perception of the therapy by the general public. It is unfortunate that in many cases the practice of aromatherapy is seen as belonging solely in the domain of the beauty parlour. This may well be so but these substances have been used for centuries to bring about the well-being of the body. That there has been no outlet for this, other than beauty salons, in recent years should not detract from the very important work these substances can achieve. They work on three levels: physical, psychological and spiritual. This alone is a unique quality. There is the general belief that because it is seen as a pampering salon treatment for ladies with a bit of leisure time, it can have no beneficial aspects when related to animals. This could not be further from the truth, as animals have a far greater innate sense and understanding than humans when it comes to plants and their extracts. We, as humans, have been civilised for far too long to be able to use our senses to know if a plant substance is good for us, right for us, or will have no effect at all. Animals simply do this purely by instinct. In that aspect alone, the use of essential oils on animals, especially forage animals such as horses, should be seen as a natural occurrence and not one of pure quackery.

That said, choosing a certain oil for a particular ailment can be an absolute minefield for the uninitiated, and mistakes can, and have, been made. The very fact that the oils have a chemical make-up means that, even as a 'natural' substance, they do, in fact, have hazards attached to their nature.

Complete volumes have been written about essential oils, what they are and what they do, but very few refer to their use on animals. Sometimes, by the time a book is published it is already nearly out of date because new discoveries are being made all the time.

This book has set out to achieve a simple goal, namely to show that the use of essential oils in the promotion of well-being, not only in the horse, but also in other animals, is a natural progression of nature. The question is, how do they work?

The Fright, Flight, Fight Response

Let us examine a natural set of circumstances for the horse – the fright, flight, fight response – and then see how the use of essential oils can assist the situation.

The fright, flight, fight response (3-F syndrome) is a basic state of body arousal brought about by threat, real or imagined. It is a primeval and primary response to the struggle for survival, originating from a time when people and animals had to cope with, and overcome, all sorts of dangers in order to survive. It is basically an alarm mechanism which prepares the individual for fighting or fleeing in order to survive a particular threat. It hinges on the need to survive and the overriding desire to reproduce and ensure the continuity of the species.

Everyone, animal or human, has their own personal triggers for this response. Although the external stimuli may be different for each of us, the basic internal physiological response is mostly the same. This means that those organs and parts of the body not needed at the time of the 3-F syndrome are shut down to maximise the response in those organs and parts that are essential to survival. For example:

- Salivation stops – drying out the mouth.
- Stomach/digestive motions are slowed to a virtual standstill and defecation and urination may take place.
- The heart beat speeds up considerably, causing blood pressure to rise.
- The increased intake of air causes breathing to become faster, making the lungs work harder.
- The adrenal glands secrete hormones such as adrenaline, enabling the body to work faster under the 3-F syndrome.

Prolonged periods of this state will cause overload on the nervous system which, in extreme cases, can break down. This will happen in greater or lesser degrees and can cause the health of the living organism – be it person or animal – to be adversely affected.

Essential oils can help this extreme state of stimulation. They can provide pain-relieving, calming influences, producing both mental and physical relief from the 3-F situation.

- Lemongrass is attributed with having a beneficial effect on the central nervous system. This oil was clinically tested in 1976 (by Seth, Kokate & Varma) and found to have similar effects to that of a tranquilliser.
- Rosemary inhibits histamine. Roman Chamomile also has this ability and is, in addition, an anti-inflammatory agent.
- Peppermint and Eucalyptus, when blended, have been shown to have mentally relaxing and muscle-relaxant effects (Gobel, Smidt & Soyka).
- Lavender, under testing, has been shown to have sedative, calming, soothing and cicatrizant effects, due mostly to the linalyl acetate in its chemical composition.
- Mandarin oil has been shown to combat restlessness.
- Petitgrain, a form of orange oil, has antispasmodic, sedative qualities and can be used on those who are highly strung.
- Neroli is a good combatant of stress and shock.
- Ravensara is an oil with many similar properties to Lavender.
- Sandalwood is an excellent nerve relaxant.

Minor symptoms of the 3-F syndrome can be experienced in varying degrees in the domesticated horse. Horses react to many frightening situations as if they were still in the wild. Treating the horse with kindness, gentleness and patience at the time of the particular trauma being experienced is very helpful, and this will, in some cases, be all that is needed to bring about a calm state again, but for others something extra will be needed to help bring about this state. Essential oils, a natural plant extract that wild equines foraged for years ago, and which horses would still forage for today if returned to the wild, are able to bring about a calmer state, reduce tension, release muscle spasm and induce feelings of calmness and balance once more.

The main benefits of oils are that, being natural ingredients, they have few or no toxic side-effects. It must be understood, however, that the term 'natural' should in no way detract from the fact that should the oils be used in an 'overdose' situation, they could pose a very real danger to the recipient.

Essential oils have therapeutic properties covering many aspects. Where they are quite unique, however, is that whilst they are combating one situation, they are very often having an effect on another. Peppermint is a prime example of this. Peppermint is used for muscle fatigue and spasm. However, it is also a stomachic and is beneficial to the digestive system, whilst at the same time having a direct effect on the respiratory system, opening up the airways and clearing the nasal cavities with its menthol action. There are not too many pharmaceutical preparations available today that enjoy such a diverse reputation.

One example of this concerns my own mare, Chance. I have been making up a respiratory preparation to help with her COPD symptoms for nearly two years now. The effects of this took six months to show a really marked improvement, but one side-effect is that her joints are more supple. Furthermore, her coat, always long and thick in winter, used to be extremely greasy. This is no longer the case. The coat gleams and shines with health and is soft to the touch. Whilst it is important to have a degree of 'grease' or natural oil on the coat to repel extremes of weather, Chance was in excess of what was naturally needed. For a mare of 24 she looks years younger and her energy levels are much higher than those of five years ago.

Another element must be taken into account when considering the use of essential oils, that of cost effectiveness. Essential oils are sold in anything from 2.5ml to 1 litre. The point to bear in mind is that 20ml of an oil is going to go a long way. One litre of Aloe Vera gel will last at least six weeks to two months on average. A litre tub of Aloe Vera gel is about £13-£15 ($9–$12). There are 200 x 5ml spoonfuls of gel in a tub. The average price of a 10ml bottle of Lavender is about £3.50 ($3). In a 10ml bottle of Lavender oil there are 200 drops of oil. When you consider that a preparation may take 4 x 5ml spoonfuls of Aloe Vera gel and 10 drops of Lavender oil, you can see it is not going to work out very expensive at all – a fact that has to be considered in every equine home I have ever known. Take into consideration also that Lavender has so many therapeutic properties for both human and equine alike and the cost effective issue becomes quite an important one. A dosage conversion table is provided on p.6.

I have been asked why, if the use of essential oils is so good, there is a need for a vet? The answer is simple. There will always be the need for mainstream conventional medicine – it is the way of progress. However, as with the complementary side, mainstream practices are not all things to all people. Something else is always needed, and using the two hand in hand is literally taking the best of both worlds and utilising them in an intelligent manner. One does not cancel out the need for the other. That said, I do believe there is one main difference between a vet and an essential oil therapist (and, indeed, other holistic practitioners). The difference, and it is purely a personal belief, is that a vet is trained to treat the symptoms that are presenting themselves at the time of examination, whilst holistic therapists are trained to look at the entity as a whole, i.e. to look at the living being (horse or human) and their circumstances, not just the presenting symptoms. When choosing an oil this will make the difference between choosing one for a physical ailment or one for an emotional issue which may be manifesting as a physical symptom.

In the end, it comes down to personal choice, and whether someone is open minded enough to explore other avenues.

CHAPTER 3

'*Aroma-Therapy*'

The Art of Smelling Essential Oils

Aromatherapy is a man-made word, and does not actually have an etymological meaning. It has now passed into popular use and, as such, is noted in the dictionary as meaning *'the massaging of skin with fragrant oils in order to relieve tension'*. The word itself was invented by Rene Gattefosse. From working with the aromatic liquids we know today as essential oils, Gattefosse realised that merely the smell of them could make a person feel better, could lift a depressive mood or just make them feel more relaxed. He termed this process aromatherapy simply because the smells were healing – 'aroma' for smell and the French word *'therapie'* for healing. Of course, it has to be said that the process is more complicated than simply smelling something nice and feeling better. An actual process is taking place whilst the aroma is being detected by the brain.

Our sense of smell is important, and whilst it is, today, more latent than it used to be, we use it far more than we consciously realise. Some people's sense of smell is far more acute than others. Aroma has a powerful influence on us as individuals. There are times when the very survival of the human race has depended upon it. The horse in the wild has also relied upon that particular sense for its continued survival. A horse can detect aroma at great distances and, like most animals, can detect the 'smell' of water from miles away. It is debatable whether water itself actually has a 'smell' but the effect it has on its environment creates smells that attract creatures from far and wide. A horse can smell the presence of another horse and especially that of an approaching human. A horse in the wild has to be able to detect different aromas on the air currents. Its very survival may depend on isolating certain smells and being prepared for what they might mean.

The sense of smell gives a living entity a heightened sense of being. Modern living has removed much of this from the human. We now tend to live in hermetically sealed boxes surrounded by mostly artificial aromas, if any at all. Horses, however, still rely upon this sense to feed information to the brain. For example, a horse can smell fear on a human or another animal. It is said to be able to smell danger. This can be a misleading term. How can danger have a smell? A predatory animal will give off a certain scent brought about by chemical reactions within the body – it is this the horse can detect. It can smell smoke, and other indefinable aromas that are not recognised and therefore could spell danger.

A horse can smell the kind of mood you are in the minute you step through the stable door – coupled with already having read your body language from the moment you stepped into view. So it is well able to give you a comprehensive 'read-out' within seconds.

Each process of living carries a particular chemical reaction which leaves its effect upon the skin. Danger or fear increases adrenaline and other such substances within us; fear will make us sweat, even if it is imperceptible to us. The sweat is released from the body through the pores of the skin, and it is this that the horse can detect, so acute is its sense of smell.

In the wild, the horse has no recourse to veterinary treatment. It cannot take itself into a veterinary practice and present itself and the problem concerned. The remedy has to be found in the wild. This is achieved via the animal's sense of smell. As a vegetarian, the horse will seek out the plant matter it needs to assuage whatever condition is presenting itself.

There are many stories concerning the horse's sense of smell, including one about a horse which found its way home from literally hundreds of miles away. Another concerns a lady in America who supposedly has a shelter full of herbs. These herbs are in tubs on racks around the walls. The horse is let into the shelter and left to browse for a period of time. Far from eating everything in sight, the horse moves around the shelter inhaling the smell of each herb and eating an amount only of the ones it actually feels it needs. Once this 'need' has been fulfilled, it no longer feeds and will leave the shelter. How much truth there is in this story, I cannot actually verify, but it does raise interesting questions and certainly goes a long way to explaining why it is that horses relate in the way they do to essential oils and herbal remedies. Humans, too, have this innate sense relating to smell, although, due to our civilisation, it is obviously much more latent than in the animal kingdom. We no longer need our sense of smell just to survive. However, that does not mean that it is not there. This is supported by an observation I have made. Each time I open my airtight box of essential oils, and there are some 40-60 oils contained therein at any one time, the nearest human will always mention one oil in particular that he or she can smell. My 10-year-old daughter can always detect ginger, while her brother at the same time detected 'a peppery smell' which turned out to be Black Pepper! Another friend can detect Garlic at a hundred paces and usually runs a mile or demands the lid be closed as she dislikes it so much. For myself, if it is in the box it will be Rose – a smell I dislike intensely and an oil I rarely use. If Rose is not in the box, I can always smell Myrrh, an aroma I simply love. It could be that if I were then to kinesiology-test the person with the oil they can smell most strongly, an imbalance would be detected somewhere within the system, or that the oil will strengthen an area not previously detected as imbalanced.

Horses, so I have found, can detect a smell around an injury. I suffer from a life-long stomach condition, inherited through my father's side. This condition will flare and subside seemingly at will, and will sometimes lie dormant for months. On days when I am suffering an acute 'attack' of this condition, my mare will often put her muzzle to my stomach and her nostrils will flare. I have also had a muscle injury to my upper arm which she has put her nose to and taken her time inhaling. Quite what it is that she can smell we will probably never know, but there is obviously a reactionary smell around injury and imbalance that some horses are able to detect.

So what is 'smell'? The technical term for this everyday word is 'olfaction'. This can best be described as *'reception-transmission-perception'*. In this process the aroma is detected, then processed by the receptor cells above the nasal cavities. The information is then transmitted to the olfactory bulb located in the cerebral cortex of the brain and on into what is known as the 'limbic system'. It is in the limbic system that the aroma is perceived and recognised. Our smell memory is vast and works far quicker than that of our photographic memory. In fact, it is almost instant. This is why we can detect certain smells and immediately make statements such as 'it reminds me of my school/childhood/grandmother'. We do not carry this information with us every day; our conscious mind simply does not have the capacity for it. In the same way that we store a computer program, so our smell memory bank is stored away in the hard drive of the limbic system!

Smell memory rarely fades, except perhaps through injury or some other incapacitating circumstance, and lasts long after other faculties have begun to fade. A far more complicated process is also happening when aromas are being detected and processed, one that is far more acute in equines than in humans. When using olfaction, each half of the brain is working, producing, in effect, two functions. This is best summed up by Figure 2.1

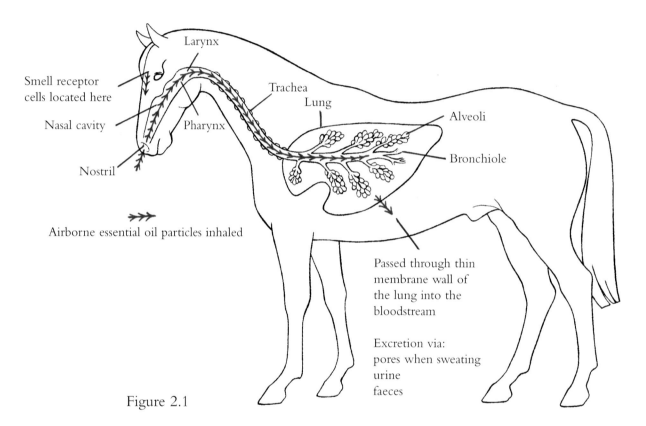

Figure 2.1

Horses use this function to great effect when inhaling the smell of essential oils. Whereas a human will smell an aroma simultaneously with both nasal cavities, the horse uses each nostril individually. When an oil is offered to the horse, it will not place its entire nose over the area of oil/aroma. It will smell first with one nostril and then the other. It will, generally, use the right nostril first, and the smell will be detected and processed through the left lobe of the brain. It will then move its left nostril over the oil/aroma, and the smell will then be detected and processed through the right lobe of the brain. It depends on the prevailing condition which nostril the horse will present over the oil/aroma first. If the horse has an imbalance in the physical sense, it will probably use its right nostril first. If the problem is more emotionally based, the horse will use its left nostril first. It is therefore important to take note of which nostril the horse uses when first presented with the essential oil. I have used the word 'probably' here as there is always the exception that proves the rule and the old adage remains of 'never work with animals or children'! Noting which nostril has been used will give you more of an indication of the nature of the presenting problem. What may have been perceived as a physical problem, say, a liver imbalance (shown through kinesiology testing) may, in fact, not be due to structural elements such as pollution, digestion of unsuitable feedstuffs, etc., but be an emotional response manifesting itself as a physical imbalance. Emotions can affect the way the liver functions. Observing the way in which the horse is detecting the aroma may allow you to approach the presenting problem in a different manner than you would otherwise have done, and to investigate what may have caused the emotional response which might otherwise have gone undetected.

Notes

An essential oil is a highly volatile substance. Volatility is the process by which a substance will evaporate on contact with the air. Essential oils do not all evaporate at the same speed. This process is broken down by perfumiers and aromatherapists into categories known as 'notes'. These, in turn, are categorised into three bands.

- **Top** notes – those aromas that evaporate on contact with the air very rapidly.
- **Base** notes – those aromas which take longer to evaporate and therefore to detect, but whose aroma will linger longest.
- In between these two categories are the **middle** notes whose aromas are a combination of the other two.

However, this is all very much open to conjecture as there is some disagreement as to what constitutes a top note or a middle or bottom note. This is due to the fact that essential oils will differ from season to season and can be affected by climate, altitude and, perhaps, the methods of extraction and storage; and also that we are, after all, individuals, and what smells a certain way to one person may not do so to another. Perception is idiosyncratic to all of us.

It is therefore best to take the top, middle or bottom note scale as a broad-based guide only. It is a useful tool, though, to assess what oils to blend together. For example, if you took, say, four base notes, this would be a heavy, heady blend, almost too much to bear and could cause headaches and sensory irritation. If you blended all top notes together, the effect would be sharp and transitory and leave you with a feeling of it being unsatisfactory. Using all middle notes could give you a blend that was very bland and not the best that it perhaps could be. Therefore, using the note table as a guide, you will be able to take a cross section of top, middle or bottom notes to produce a blend that is pleasing and effective.

The following is only a short guide to a number of top, middle and bottom notes.

Top notes:

Bergamot, Lavender, Lemon, Lime, Mandarin, Neroli, Grapefruit

Middle notes:

Ginger, Lemongrass, Sweet Marjoram, Jasmine, Rose

Base notes:

Sandalwood, Frankincense, Myrrh, Vetiver, Violet Leaf

There is a misconception that 'note' refers to the aroma of an oil rather than its volatility. For example, the heavy heady notes, such as Violet Leaf and Vetiver, are considered to be base notes because they have such a heavy aroma. Whilst this is true to a certain extent, it must be remembered that the term 'note' is referring to the volatility (evaporation on contact with air) of an oil.

The question must also be asked then – can an essential oil be taken into the body simply by inhaling? The answer is yes it can. Once opened to the air the oil becomes volatile (evaporates) and the evaporating process begins immediately. The released particles, which are microscopic, are inhaled through the nose, where they are warmed and moistened. Small hairs, known as the cilia, then pass the tiny particles along the nasal cavity to the olfactory receptor cells (located in the bridge of the nose area, or in the soft tissue of the area under the part of the face where a horse's blaze would show). Each olfactory cell has a nerve fibre which leads from the main body of the cell, and along this a chemical message is sent to the main olfactory bulb, connected to the limbic system situated on the frontal lobe of the brain. The inhalation process then passes the microscopic particles down the body through the larynx, pharynx, trachea, and on into the lungs. They are then passed through the walls of the lungs and excreted as sweat, or on the breath, or through urine and faeces. This method of ingestion is quicker to work but shorter lived than that of an oil that is applied to the skin where it will eventually be absorbed into the bloodstream.

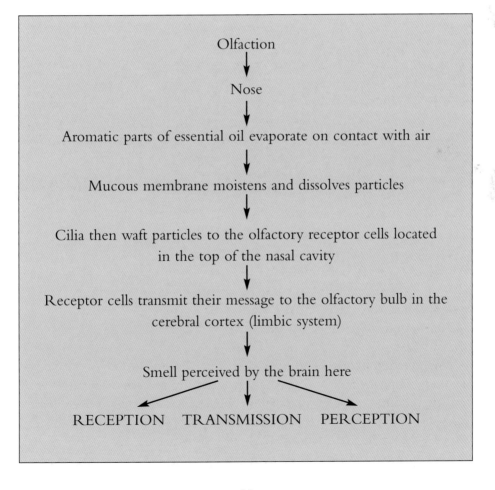

Olfaction

↓

Nose

↓

Aromatic parts of essential oil evaporate on contact with air

↓

Mucous membrane moistens and dissolves particles

↓

Cilia then waft particles to the olfactory receptor cells located
in the top of the nasal cavity

↓

Receptor cells transmit their message to the olfactory bulb in the
cerebral cortex (limbic system)

↓

Smell perceived by the brain here

RECEPTION   TRANSMISSION   PERCEPTION

The Emotive Effect of Smells

One last word on smell – or olfaction. As we know, smell is very emotive. Smell can make us feel an emotion. I was born in November. I am always drawn to the damp, earthy, woody aromas of autumn, such as Vetiver, Rosewood, Sandalwood, Myrrh, Ginger and Cinnamon. I perceive all of these as autumn/winter smells. Is it because I was born in these months that I favour them over the summer months? I am drawn to the smells of winter far sooner than I am to those of summer, a season I find can be quite enervating. It would be interesting to undertake a detailed study and observe if those born in summer were more drawn to smells such as Geranium, Rose or Lavender, say, or if those born in spring might like the sharper, lighter smells of Sweet Orange, Grapefruit or Lemon. Observe your horse – to what season does it belong in the sense of smell? Will it respond to these oils far better than to those of another season? Are we all, at the end of the day, human or animal, governed by need or by our roots, the time we came into being and first learnt to use our senses? Are we far more governed by our sense of smell, as is our equine counterpart, than we have ever given ourselves credit for?

Our sense of smell is a potent one. Through the use of essential oils on a regular basis you may find that your sense of smell becomes more acute and is carried over into other areas. Who knows, we may yet learn once again to be as sensitive as our equine counterparts.

CHAPTER 4

Safety Guidelines for the Use of Essential Oils

It is a misconception to believe that because essential oils are deemed to be a 'natural' product, there is no hazard connected to their use. This is not so. These substances can be very hazardous and, if misused, can cause toxicity, sensitisation and even death. This chapter comprehensively covers aspects of safety and I cannot recommend highly enough that it should be read thoroughly and its contents remembered and, most important of all, understood.

We have a duty of care to our animals. They are not able to turn round and tell us that they are having an adverse reaction to an oil that has too strong a dilution, or is a dermal irritant, or has caused a systemic reaction. By the time we are actually aware that there might be a problem, it is too late and the animal has suffered because of our lack of care and/or understanding. This is not an acceptable event under any circumstances. Please read and digest the following very carefully and thoroughly.

Buying Oils

When you purchase your essential oils make sure that you are buying them from a reputable source. High street outlets, in the form of gift shops, new age shops or garden centres, are not always the best place for this. I will be held as very unpopular for that view but there are sound reasons behind this opinion.

Essential oil suppliers sell only the freshest oils, kept in the correct conditions and bottled and posted to you usually within 48 hours of your order being placed. Furthermore, they normally come by specialist carrier rather than normal post. Age, condition, storage, carriage – all these have an effect on an oil. It is a delicately balanced substance. If you are buying at the end of a chain (i.e. manufacturer–supplier–warehouse–outlet–purchaser), you cannot always guarantee how long the oil has been kept at each stage of its journey, or under what conditions. Always try to buy the very best that you can afford, from a knowledgeable and reputable supplier. The other advantage of talking to the supplier direct, of course, is that their advice, should you seek it (and you should if ever you are in doubt), will be accurate – they will know their product. These suppliers are dealing with the raw materials; they are aware of what these oils do. If you are in any doubt at all as to which oil to buy, i.e. which Chamomile – there are at least three – or which Peppermint, of which there are many, the essential oil supplier will be able to advise you, based on the information you have given them. Most reputable suppliers will also send out an information sheet on the oil you have purchased. Sometimes these are free, although some companies do make a nominal charge for this. Whilst they do not cost very much, they are invaluable for reference purposes.

Cost is another important factor to bear in mind. It can be a good gauge of what standard of oil you are buying. I purchased a 10ml bottle of Neroli from a UK new-age-type gift shop, intrigued by the price which seemed very low. When I inspected the oil at home, and did a patch test with it, it became obvious that it was adulterated to a considerable extent and that the oil contained virtually no natural energy whatsoever. It went into my next bath and was very pleasant but completely unsuitable for my work purposes. Ask the suppliers for their price lists and compare prices but, most of all, try to retain in your mind a rough guideline of what you should be paying for certain oils. If an oil is £5 ($3.62) for 10ml and you see it in a retail outlet for half the price, you can almost certainly rest assured that it is adulterated. Adulteration is the process whereby an expensive oil is added to a cheaper one, or pure alcohol is added to 'stretch' it. This completely alters the delicate chemical balance and it will not have the therapeutic values attributed to an unadulterated oil.

Keeping Oils

Once you have taken the time to buy your essential oils, do not then throw them in a drawer or box with a whole variety of tack and grooming articles that are kept in less than ideal temperatures or standards of cleanliness. The oils should be kept in a cool, darkened, temperate place of safe keeping. Do not keep them in the kitchen as the temperature there fluctuates too much. Do not keep them in the fridge as this is an extreme of temperature and could have an adverse effect on the balance of the oil. Keep the bottles upright. Bottles that are laid on their side may not have the cap on correctly, or tight enough, or the cap may be damaged. There may be a seepage of oil around the neck of the bottle. This will oxidise and will taint the rest of the oil coming out, and could have an adverse reaction on the recipient.

In Chapter 9, when talking about the home essential oil kit, I discuss suitable containers. If you are only going to keep one, two or maybe three bottles of oil at any one time, you do not need to go to the expense of buying an airtight container. As long as you ensure that the oils are kept upright in a safe location, they should be fine. An alternative would be to keep them in a small tin, be it a cake tin or baking tin, or even a sturdy cardboard box. If, however, you embrace more wholly the concept of complementary theories and wish to purchase a number of oils, it really is best that you find a suitable airtight container as soon as possible after purchasing the oils. This could be an aluminium camera case which can be bought at a reasonable price from DIY outlets in the UK. Hard plastic tool boxes, with cantilevered shelves, also make suitable containers. The main aspect of these types of container is that they are normally of sufficient weight and sturdiness to remain upright when travelling in the car, or if kicked. Remember to keep the bottles upright at all times as prevention is always better than cure.

Keep a sheaf of record forms handy. Recording when you purchased each oil is always a good idea. Oils deteriorate once they have been opened. Some obviously deteriorate quicker than others. Work on the premise that most essential oils will last a year once opened, with all Citrus oils being given a six-month shelf life once opened. I mark on the bottle label which month I bought the oil and this serves as a constant reminder to check the oils as I am using them. That said, I have to say that some oils simply do last a long time without any apparent diminishable effect. Patchouli is one of these oils. I have had a bottle for four years, which had been pushed to a dark and nether region of the metal container I use, and, upon inspection, has been fine. I have used it; it smells wonderful and still has a very positive energy about it. Investigation has shown that this is one of the few oils that actually improves with age. I have found other oils that have gone over the one year average and have still worked well. However, it is not a recommended option, and I would still advise changing an oil after a year.

Temperature is a very important aspect in the storage and keeping of essential oils. Keeping them in an airing cupboard (as one client did) because they are safe there is not a very good option to choose! The heat will cause a shift in the delicate chemical balance and I believe this will affect the efficacy of the oil.

Do not keep them in the fridge, as I mentioned earlier, in the belief that this will preserve them for longer, especially during a long hot summer. Again, the balance will be affected and, having experimented with this myself, I find that the energy of the oil alters considerably and does not return once warmed through again.

Do not leave the oils in direct sunlight. There are two schools of thought on this point. One says that it has no direct effect upon the oil at all. However, having seen what happens to a bottle of olive oil that has been left on a window sill in full sunlight, and how quickly that oil turned sour and cloudy – I have to beg to differ. The other school of thought believes that oils should not be exposed to ultra violet rays of the sun. We protect our skins – why not these delicate oils?

Keep all oils out of the reach of children – *at all times*. Children are fascinated by the enticing smell of the oils – after all some of them actually smell like food – Grapefruit, Sweet Orange, Lemon and Lime, for instance. Children will be tempted to try them orally. This is highly dangerous. In the event of this happening, wash the mouth out immediately with warm water and call a doctor, whether the child appears to be fine or not. Children should not be allowed to handle the bottles of oil either. These oils are highly concentrated substances and some are severe dermal irritants – Ginger and Garlic, for instance. The skin of children is highly sensitive and susceptible. It is always better to be safe than sorry. Eucalyptus oil, for example, is so toxic that, if taken orally, as little as 3ml of undiluted oil can kill an adult, let alone a child.

Keep your stock of oils to a minimum or to those that you *know* you will use. Having 20 oils in a box might look impressive but it is a false economy if you are only ever going to use a basic half dozen of them. Added to which, I have not entered an equine establishment yet where pennies are not counted to within the last important one! So do not waste money on oils that will just sit there and become surplus to requirements after a year.

Using Oils

- Never exceed a stated dose that may be given to you. An essential oil is a highly concentrated substance. If it is recommended that you use only six drops, then do so. Whilst you may not think it appears very much, if it is the recommended level advised to you, then stick to it. One drop of oil in 5ml of carrier may seem as nothing at all. If, however, that is the amount advised for that particular oil (Vetiver and Violet Leaf spring to mind here) on a particular horse, there is a very good reason for it. Some oils induce an emotional healing crisis (see above, and add Yarrow or Rose to that). Little and often may be a far better and safer method for your horse than a large, one-off dose that it is simply not able to cope with. Remember that essential oils can be up to one hundred times more concentrated *after* extraction from the plant. Use them with the utmost care.

- Do not apply undiluted essential oils directly onto the skin – yours, another human's or your horse's. Always dilute in a carrier (i.e. gel/cream/lotion/oil/shampoo, etc.). You may read in certain places that Lavender and Tea Tree are fine to put on undiluted. I would not recommend this to anyone using oils at home. It simply is not worth the risk. A practitioner may well choose to do this, but he or she is working from experience and with a great deal more knowledge than the average person wishing to use these oils at home. I cannot recommend this at all.

- Do not apply oils to the areas around the eyes, genitalia or the inside of the nostrils. This could cause a severe dermal reaction, and, if applied direct to the mucous membranes, could cause serious damage. There is one tale of a young lady who, on finding an oil to be attributed with aphrodisiac properties, applied the oil neat to her boyfriend's genitalia. This was not followed by a night of passion but a painful sojourn to hospital. Do not even think about it.

- Do not store essential oils near a naked flame; these are extremely flammable substances.

- Do not store essential oils near machinery. The vibrations can upset the delicate balance of the oils. The term 'machinery' includes such items as washing machines, tumbler dryers, fridges, freezers, dishwashers, etc.

- Never leave the lid off the bottle of essential oil or of a blend that you have made up. The oils will evaporate as soon as they are exposed to the air. Prolonged exposure will cause oxidisation, as mentioned earlier.

Also ensure that the correct cap goes on the correct bottle to prevent cross contamination of oils.

- Do not allow oils to be removed by, or used on your horses by, anyone else. It is a basic safety precaution that should always be heeded.

- In the event that your skin comes into contact with undiluted oils, wash the area thoroughly immediately. This will minimise the risk of irritation or sensitisation on the area. Also wash eyes and nose areas thoroughly immediately after contact. After washing with water I have found that the immediate application of a generous amount of Aloe Vera gel helps the situation greatly. Accidents do happen, even to the best of us, but what you do immediately after the accident is vital. The situation of a neat oil being accidentally spilled onto a horse should **never** happen, as oils should never be mixed in the vicinity of the animal. However, the same rules apply.

- There is an opinion that oils should be kept in dark glass bottles. There is also the opinion that storing the oils in clear glass bottles has no detrimental effect upon them. This may be so, but I personally prefer to use opaque glass to prolong the life of the oil or blend. I would recommend that you do the same until such time as there is clear scientific evidence to the contrary. Sunlight is a very powerful source of energy. It can turn things sour in such a short space of time. Items fade. Imagine what sunlight would do to an oil stored in clear glass. I advocate not taking the chance. Use opaque glass and err on the side of caution.

- Always ensure that the essential oils you buy have dropper inserts. If they do not, buy them. They cost next to nothing, but, from a safety point of view, are absolutely invaluable. You simply cannot gauge the true amount of the drops being used by pouring straight from the bottle. Pipettes can also be used for this purpose.

- Always wipe around the neck of a bottle after use, whether it is the bottle of neat essential oil or a bottle containing a blend or a carrier oil. Even if a bottle containing undiluted oil has a dropper insert, highly mobile oils, such as Juniper, come out quickly and can splash and, as the bottle is turned upright again, an amount of oil invariably dribbles down the neck. Even thicker oils, such as Benzoin, can leave a residue. It is vital this is wiped away to keep the bottle pure.

- Never apply the same blend of oil to any horse other than the one it is mixed for, unless directed to do so by a therapist. Keep horses' blends separate. What suits one may well not suit another.

- **Never** leave glass bottles around the stable or yard. Broken glass will cause any amount of damage. Do not keep the bottles in your pocket whilst working around the yard. It is all too easy to drop them in the bedding where they can be trodden or lain on by the horse. Do not 'just pop' the bottle onto a ledge in the stable either. Activity around a stable yard is often busy – it would be all too easy to forget that you have put it there. Should this fall into the bedding, or not have a top on it, or the horse takes it in its mouth, the results would be very serious indeed. Try to find someone to hold the bottle/jar/container for you and then put it directly away.
- If offering a bottle containing a blend to a horse for it to inhale, do not hold it too close and keep it held firmly down within the fist. The horse may well try to take the bottle in its mouth. It needs little imagination to explain what could happen not if, but *when,* the bottle breaks.
- Always ensure that your horse is not contra-indicated (unable to take the blend or oil) to the oils that you are proposing to use. It is imperative that you ensure that the oil does not compromise any other homoeopathic/clinical remedy being taken (i.e. Peppermint is so strong that it antidotes homoeopathic remedies. Jasmine is credited with having parturient properties – meaning it can induce foaling contractions. It would be inadvisable, therefore, to use this on a pregnant mare. Do not use oils over an open wound; use them in the locality. If in doubt over this aspect, always seek advice from a reputable source such as a vet or a therapist.
- Always ensure that your blends are clearly, securely and correctly labelled so that you know exactly what a bottle contains, who it is for, what it is for, and the date it was made up. You may think that you will remember how much of which oil you used and in what carrier. The reality is that you will not.
- Never apply oils with dirty hands. Wash and dry them before and afterwards. The reasons for this are obvious.
- When applying a blend to an injury site, do not apply direct with the fingers and then take more of the blend out of the pot. This can cause a bacterial infection. One way is to use double-ended cotton buds, using each end only once – once into the blend, once onto the area around the injury site, i.e. mud fever, sweet itch, scrapes and grazes, etc. A clean end or bud should then be used.
- Never use oils on an injury site that has not been thoroughly cleaned and dried first. Even the smallest of nicks should be thoroughly cleaned

before the oils are applied. Keep a bottle of Hibiscrub around the yard, together with a container used only for that purpose. One capful of Hibiscrub per cupful of water is sufficient. Use cotton wool pads to cleanse the area and dry with a square of clean old towel kept for that purpose.

- Do not attempt to use these oils on, or to massage, a horse that is not properly restrained – even a horse you think you know well. The horse may jolt in surprise, you may drop the bottle, it could get trodden on and so could you. Avoid hazardous situations by using common sense.
- *Never* try to mix essential oils with cold water – they are insoluble in water. Always use a carrier and, if water is to be used, make sure you add a surfactant (an agent that promotes bonding, available from all essential oil suppliers) in a sufficient amount for the blend.
- Do not make up blends for other horses for use by other people. It would be all too easy to do this once you have been using the oils for a while and think you understand them. Only trained therapists can do this. Training courses are readily available and come in all guises to suit all people and all financial situations. Trained essential oil therapists are also insured for what they do. Civilians are not. Essential oil therapy is a complicated subject. This book is a guidebook only, for those wishing to use oils at home on their own horses. It is not a training manual that, once read, means you are an essential oil therapist. Please bear this point very much in mind before you embark upon a course of action you may later come to regret.
- This chapter has referred in parts to 'irritation' and 'sensitisation'. They are similar but not quite the same. The table below sets out the chain of events that could lead to irritation and sensitisation through misuse of oils.

Irritation	Sensitisation
Oil absorbed into the skin reacts with mast cells and releases histamine into the system.	Allergic skin reaction to essential oil takes the form of a rash similar to urticaria. Oil penetrates skin. Can occur after one use or with constant use over a period of time. Reaction not dose dependent.

Irritation	Sensitisation
Refers to localised inflammation which affects skin and mucous membranes (i.e. inside nostrils).	Immune response releases histamine.
Results in itchiness and varying degrees of inflammation.	Causes an inflammatory reaction by cells of immune system.
Caused by using undiluted oils or in high concentration – depends on individual and may be idiosyncratic.	First exposure = slight reaction, repeated application = skin inflammation (blotchy and irritated).
	Not dose or concentration dependent.
Examples: Sweet Basil, Black Pepper	*Examples: Ginger, Peppermint*

Admittedly, these are the reactions attributed to the human body. However, one must reasonably assume that as the equine shares almost the same body systems as the human, the reaction, if not the same, would be very similar.

- Some essential oils are toxic. Toxicity is serious. In fact, one has to wonder why an oil that is a known toxic and has no use in essential oil therapy is ever produced. It is as well, however, to be aware of toxic oils and their effects.

<table>
<tr><th colspan="2" align="center">Toxicity</th></tr>
</table>

Acute Refers to severe reaction to an allergen or oil Reactions include damage to renal organs due to the filtering action they perform within the body.	**Chronic** Refers to longstanding application of a substance. Reactions include prolonged headaches, sickness, severe skin reactions.

Toxic oils include:

Aniseed	*Mugwort*	*Thuga*
Penny Royal	*Cinnamon Leaf*	*Eucalyptus*
Thyme		

As you can see, some of the oils on the toxic list also appear on the list of essential oils recommended for use in this book. This does not mean that they cannot be used but that they should be used with the utmost care and in a very high (more carrier to oil) dilution.

Hazardous Oils

There are some oils that should never be used in essential oil therapy at all. These include the following:

Bitter Almond	*Aniseed*	*Arnica*
Boldo	*Cassia*	*Camphor*
Cinnamon Bark	*Costus*	*Elecampane*
Bitter Fennel	*Horseradish*	*Mugwort*
Mustard	*Origanum*	*Penny Royal*
Dwarf Pine	*Sage*	*Sassafras*
Savin	*Savory*	*Tansy*
Thuga	*Wormseed*	

It is highly unlikely that you will ever come across these oils, certainly you should not find them in a high street retail outlet, and a reputable supplier, whilst they may have some in stock, would definitely ask why you require that oil. Whilst you may never come across, or indeed purchase, any of the oils on the hazardous list, forewarned is forearmed. Be vigilant and be aware. The safety of you and your horse depends on it.

Phototoxicity

This is a systemic reaction that occurs when an oil is applied and the area of application is then exposed to the sun. This can cause severe burns on the skin in humans. The same applies to horses, especially in the delicate area of the muzzle and, of course, on greys. Phototoxic oils are usually the Citric oils, those that are cold-expressed from the skin of the fruit. Such oils include Bergamot, Tangerine, Lemon, Lime, Grapefruit and Sweet and Bitter Orange. Non-Citrus oils that carry this effect are Opoponax (a similar oil to Myrrh) and Verbena. In severe cases, blistering or deep weeping burns may occur.

Bergamot, Lemon and Grapefruit, among others, are also on the recommended list in this book. These are valuable oils with great therapeutic properties. A degree of care and thought is required in their use to avoid sensitisation. The presence of furocoumarins in the oil, such as Bergamot (chemical constituent, Bergaptene) causes this reaction, and it is possible to purchase a furocoumarins-free Bergamot oil. As it is a useful oil in fly repellent and insect bite blends, due to its pruritic value (prevents itching), this is worth bearing in mind when purchasing.

Parts of this chapter may sound alarming and leave you wondering if, indeed, it is safe to use essential oils on horses at all. There are many situations when essential oils can be used and to great advantage. The oils on the recommended list in this book have been chosen with great care and a lot of thought. Knowledge is power. This chapter on safety is a good point of reference in all your dealings with essential oils. Essential oils can be used in the following siuations, provided dilution levels are adhered to and not exceeded and provided that you assess your horse carefully before embarking on the use of these oils.

Massage

A good way of connecting with your horse and forging deeper communication levels, helping you to understand each other more. Avoid injury sites and bruised areas (if known).

After a Day's Hunting

There will be times when a quick rub down will not be enough for your horse, especially as it gets older, or if the going was hard. A muscle wash is very much in order under these circumstances.

Dressage

Sustained controlled movement, coupled with a nervous disposition or awareness of its rider's nerves, can leave a horse both physically and mentally exhausted. Gentle massage with sedative, relaxing oils in a wash is very much a recovery aid in this instance.

Horses on Box Rest

Box rest can be a potentially depressing time for a horse, especially one who prefers being turned out. A gentle massage with an uplifting oil, such as Bergamot, would be beneficial to the horse's well-being.

Products

Fly repellents, sweet itch lotions, mud fever preparations – all these and more can be safely prepared and used.

Arthritis and Rheumatism

Acidic conditions such as these can be greatly assisted by the application of essential oils in correct dilutions in a massage lotion or gel.

Pain Relief

I have used oils in a gentle head massage after dental work (1 drop in 5ml carrier). The effects have been almost instant.

If in doubt, always contact a therapist. Advice is free.

CHAPTER 5

Essential Oils

What they are and what they are not
30 essential oils and their therapeutic uses
Hydrolats – what they are and when to use them

What They Are and What They Are Not

So far we have covered the potted history of essential oils, a reason to use them, how to smell them and how to use them safely. But what are they – and more to the point, what are they not? Firstly, they are a therapeutically attributed plant extract used to bring about a holistic state of balance in the body and mind. They are a means of bringing about the subtle balance which keeps us healthy both physiologically and psychologically. What they are not is a cure-all that negates the need for conventional mainstream medicines and remedies. There are those who now wish to find another way, other than the sometimes invasive chemicals of mainstream medicines and drugs and their toxic effects. Essential oils allow that to take place, at least in part.

There are times when it is not convenient or wise to visit the doctor for minor cuts and bruises, strained muscles or ailments such as colds and flu-like viruses. The prescription of antibiotics has now been very much curtailed due to overuse, lessening their effects. If we were to run to the doctor's surgery for every minor ailment known to man, he or she would have to work 24 hours a day and we would probably be queuing down the street at open surgery time. Either that or looking for a new practice to enlist with because we had been asked to leave by a poor overworked doctor!

In the veterinary world costs can be prohibitive. Vets' call-out fees, especially in city areas and, conversely, more remote ones, can be so high that some horse/animal owners not only *do* think twice about calling the vet out but, financially, have no other option. What, then, is the alternative, if any? This is where I feel complementary therapies, such as essential oil therapy, play a very important role in our lives. Do we call the vet out if our horse seems under the weather? Can most of us afford the expensive call-out fee only to be told 'your horse is just under the weather'? I doubt it. Those who can very often are not taken seriously when something *is* wrong.

Essential oil therapy is known as a complementary therapy – it enhances not replaces. A high proportion of doctors and vets dismiss essential oil therapy, and refuse to attribute any significant power to the oils, other than a psychosomatic response to the aroma – not realising that this actually *is* the direct response of the limbic system to an external stimulus – namely the volatile oil particles being breathed in and processed. But what of the psychosomatic response? If something makes you feel better and therefore you do get better – *because* you feel better – what is wrong in that? The mind is a wondrous thing – it has enormous power and we must all know of at least one incident in our lives where we have known or witnessed sheer willpower achieving something.

Unfortunately, not enough medical-based scientific research is devoted to studying the therapeutic effects of essential oils and therefore it is very often dismissed as 'quackery'. 'It's just in the mind' is a response reported to me to have been said by so many doctors and, yes, even vets. The point that seems to be overlooked here is just how much influence the mind has over the body. The mind and its state at a given time can have a direct effect on the body, manifesting as a physical symptom – ulcers, tension headaches, stomach cramps, increased bowel and bladder movements. You can treat a physical symptom, but if it is caused by an emotional response to a problem then you are not dealing with the root cause and the problem simply refuses to go away. Ergo, you can treat a stomach complaint with Peppermint until the cows come home and achieve very poor results. That is because it may not be a physical ailment at all, but a stress-related emotional one and, say, Valerian, Vetiver or even Lavender may be better for it. So, using Peppermint is treating the symptom not the cause. In effect, we are governed by our mind and, if you like, our psyche. So are horses, perhaps even more so as they seem to me far more in touch with themselves than most humans I encounter.

Our response to a given situation, whether we are horse or human, is first noted in the brain – whether it be a conscious or subconscious thought, the effect will be the same. Somewhere down the chain of that event is the physical response to that mental stimulus – be it nausea, stomach cramps, shallow breathing, muscle spasm, increased bowel movements, nervous headaches, loss of appetite – the list is endless. In the horse, the bowel movements may become very loose, it may start to weave, it may begin to develop a trait it did not have before, it may take against anyone carrying, say, a broom – if the experience it has had with that object has been a bad one, then why shouldn't it? More often than not, the horse's behaviour is termed 'neurotic', and it is. It is a neurosis. It does not mean to say, however, that were it to be worked on and the neurosis targeted, the 'neurotic' behaviour would continue. As the horse 'let go' of the problem, then so the response to the broom would also dissipate, if not vanish altogether.

Essential oils, which can have a direct effect on the central nervous system and a sedative effect on our psyche, can help the horse. It is part of what I do for a living, so I know this works. What, in effect, is being discussed here is the fright, fight, flight response which is a mental stimulus manifesting itself in physical symptoms, as was mentioned in the previous chapter.

I have offered a weak solution of Violet Leaf to an overstrung horse and watched it have an instant effect – the head drops, the ears relax, the eyes go soft and heavy and a huge exhalation of breath occurs. Violet Leaf and Vetiver are such wonderfully grounding oils, their effect being immediately felt in the chest cavity, and, having inhaled them myself, I know that feeling of being connected once more to the earth.

When humans visit aromatherapists for a body massage, it is normally because of a condition of one type or another. Rarely is it just for the pampering of time alone and a pleasant activity, even if it may appear that way. There is often a subconscious need to connect with someone. Northern Europeans are not known for their social touching and the British, in particular, are quite a cellular people. Unconsciously, when we book one of those treatments, we are acting upon a need to connect with another understanding being. If you watch them as a herd, collectively or mutually grooming each other, almost shoulder to shoulder sometimes as they graze, horses have and understand this need. In connecting with another, we are already repairing part of whatever the problem is. Adding essential oils into that equation is also answering an almost subconscious need. Horses forage for the plants they need, almost inherently understanding which ones will alleviate which problem. Humans do the same when they book a massage. It has been a stressful week, say, they are upset and an inbuilt need to take away the tension takes over. The massage gives them the connection. They ask for Lavender oil – they know it relaxes them – they know that their inner self will feel calmer, more rational, that their skin will feel soft and smooth – they know that after that hour of connecting with someone via touch, they will feel better. The therapist understands the nature of his or her client and will perhaps add Bergamot to the blend for its therapeutic property of being able to lift the spirits. Thus we have a client who is taken out of a state of tension and whose central nervous system can come out of overwork and relax.

You will see from the ensuing list of essential oils just how many therapeutic values are attributed to these plant extracts. They are the answer to everyday minor problems and ailments and, with a regular, regulated use, can ensure long-term health. Prevention is always better than cure.

What essential oils are not, however, is a quick fix cure. We cannot overload the system with them, just as we cannot take six aspirin when the recommended dose is a maximum of two! They cannot be used on a casual basis of 'Well, Lavender was recommended but I only have Bergamot, that'll do, they're all the same'.

They are not all the same and, as I have discussed earlier, oils are extremely potent substances. It is not possible to use them undiluted and not expect consequences as a result of that action. As you would respect a pharmaceutical medical product by heeding dosage and administration and keeping it safe from prying eyes and the hands of children, so essential oils must be afforded the same respect.

30 Essential Oils and their Therapeutic Uses

Listed below are 30 essential oils with a brief resumé of their therapeutic uses.

These are the main core of oils that you would ever use at home, although hundreds more are available. However, unless you are a therapist, it seems pointless sending you out to buy in 60 oils when you will only ever use maybe a third of that! Read each resumé carefully and understand what each oil can do and, equally importantly, why it is used.

Note: the word 'mobile' is used in aromatherapy when referring to an oil that will pour extremely easily. Therefore, as a matter of course, the bottles should have dropper inserts to regulate the correct number of drops being used.

BENZOIN
Styrax benzoin

Idiosyncratic sensitisation in some, otherwise non–irritant and non–toxic.
Extraction: solvent-extracted from the resin of a tree grown in Thailand. This can be thick and almost sticky. The concrete is usually dissolved in alcohol to make it usable. It can also be bought as a resin and heated to melt as needed. If the bottle is not sealed properly, the leakage will dry to a crystalline substance and make the bottle very difficult to open, so keep the lid on tight and wipe around the top of the bottle with a clean tissue after each use.

This is not strictly an essential oil but a resinoid, although it is commonly referred to as an oil.

I absolutely adore this oil and find its aroma very emotionally satisfying. It calms and soothes and seems to produce one of those deep contented sighs from far within. The aroma is that of sweet (but not cloying) incense, emotive of the Eastern cultures and, for me, of Christmas spices. Obviously, then, another 'winter' oil!

I use Benzoin most specifically for emotional issues as it calms nervous and upset horses so quickly, without having a sedative effect. It can be used for respiratory ailments, although, personally, I tend towards other oils for this.

I do use it in muscle lotions for arthritis and rheumatism, which has the added effect of settling out the emotions. The one other use I keep it for is its styptic properties, along with Geranium and Myrrh – all are excellent at arresting external bleeding.

Benzoin is not expensive but neither is it an oil you will need a vast quantity of, so 10-20ml at a time would be more than adequate.

BERGAMOT
Citrus bergamia

Non-toxic and non-irritant when used in high dilution, requiring more carrier to essential oil.

Bergamot contains a substance called furocoumarin, which makes it extremely phototoxic (affected by exposure to sunlight). It is possible, however, to buy FCF Bergamot which is furocoumarin-free and significantly reduces the risk of phototoxic reactions. The FCF oil is obviously slightly more expensive than the original oil. However, I am about to stick my neck out here. I do not believe in tampering with what nature has provided. If it is phototoxic, then it must simply be used accordingly. The oil that has not had the furocoumarins extracted does, to me, smell nicer, and I always get a better result with it than with an oil that has been, to all intents and purposes 'doctored'. In fly repellent mixtures Bergamot does run the risk of causing reaction to sunlight, especially on greys, and this has to be taken into account. I do not use Bergamot often in fly repellents as I find other oils do the job more efficiently, although Bergamot is good for itching. It is an oil that is cold-expressed from the rind of the fruit.

This is another lovely oil that simply radiates the smell of early summer. It always makes me think of May and June when everything is still quite new and fresh and has not yet accumulated the dustiness of a hot summer. It is not surprising then that Bergamot is the major oil for lifting the spirits and I have never been let down by it. It works on people or horses – the results are the same. (I used Bergamot and Frankincense together in a blend for a friend who lost both of her horses to yew poisoning. The two working in tandem helped her to cope with her grief and sadness over the situation.) This is a good oil for cuts, wounds and skin conditions (obviously never undiluted). Bergamot is a good stomachic, soothing and settling, and I have known it be used as an aperitif, although I have to be honest and say I have never used it in this capacity myself. This oil is also a booster for the immune system, and would therefore be good for use through winter periods or spells of illness.

One of the main properties of Bergamot is its pruritic ability – it arrests itching. I therefore sometimes use it in sweet itch preparations, but mostly on wasp and bee stings and insect bites. As with many of the citric oils, it has numerous therapeutic properties. It aids and stimulates digestion, combats toxicity, is a good oil for intestinal worms (anthelmintic), has pain-relieving qualities, is very antiseptic and heals wounds. It is also an oil that has begun to gain written coverage for its use against tumours.

Tumours are not that common, I understand, in horses, more so in humans and other animals. However, at the time of writing I do know of one horse with a suspected tumour, who, when offered Bergamot, virtually snatched the bottle out of the owner's hand. Actions, as they say, often speak louder than words. Bergamot can also be used as a laxative and has diuretic properties. It is a good oil for combating urinary infections and parasites and is a general tonic. Bergamot is also effective in combating airborne bacteria and so would be useful in a spray for the stables.

On an emotional level it is good for anxiety, despondency, lack of confidence and stress. May be bought in amounts of up to 20ml bearing in mind it has a shelf life of 6 months.

BLACK PEPPER
Piper nigrum

This oil can be an irritant if used in concentration, otherwise non-toxic and non-sensitising.
Due to its strength, do not use if using homoeopathic remedies.
Extraction: steam-distilled from the black peppercorns which have previously been dried and then crushed.

This is another oil that belongs in my 'winter' category – it even smells warming. There is simply no mistaking the peppery aroma of this oil, which, if inhaled, quickly has an effect in the centre of the chest cavity.

Whilst this oil has many attributable therapeutic properties, I use it mainly in massage solutions. Black Pepper is a deep muscle relaxant, reaching the inner depths rather than just the surface area of the muscle concerned. It is an excellent oil for arthritis and rheumatism and general muscular aches and pains. Black Pepper is a circulatory stimulant and is therefore good for all forms of stiffness. As I mentioned earlier, the oil is quick to show an effect in the chest cavity and is a good oil to use for massage when a horse has become wet or cold. Because of its relaxant effect on smooth muscle, it is a good stomachic, aiding digestion, relieving colicky symptoms, stimulating the appetite and combating spasm. This is also an immuno-stimulant oil which promotes general health and well-being. Black Pepper has mild pain-relieving qualities, is rubefacient (stimulating local blood circulation), is bactericidal, antiseptic and combats microbial activity within the body. A definite oil for winter massage and muscle sprains and strains after excessive physical activity. Buy 10ml to start with.

CARROT SEED
Daucus carota

Non-toxic, non-irritant and non-sensitising.
Horses, surprise, surprise, like this oil! Although carrots are grown worldwide, the bulk of the essential oil is produced in France. The oil is extracted by steam distillation from the carrot seeds.

Where horses are concerned, this oil is said to be a natural anthelmintic – an agent that dispels intestinal worms. This would therefore be a good on-going back up to the normal and regular worming programme (Garlic is also an excellent anthelmintic). It is also an oil with 'hepatic' properties, being very beneficial to the liver. It is a cell regenerative oil and so helps in healing and 'rebuilding'. It is a toxin-buster, aids acidic conditions such as arthritis and rheumatism and is good for the circulation. Carrot Seed is a stimulant and a tonic. This makes it a good general, all round oil and it should be part of your home essential oil kit.

It has to be said that few horses have rejected this oil, and horses will show interest in my hands literally hours after I have used it. Definitely one for the box! Buy in quanties up to 20ml.

THE CHAMOMILES
Roman Chamomile – *Anthemis nobilis*
German Chamomile – *Chamomilia matricaria*

Non-toxic, non-irritant but can be idiosyncratically sensitising.
Extraction: both are steam-distilled from the fresh flowering heads of the plant.

I tried to separate these two oils, perhaps to choose one over the other, but in the end I decided that the two actually go hand in hand and that it will come down to a case of personal preference when deciding which one to use – although I always keep both. They are so closely associated it really would be quite difficult to advise on one over the other. The main difference that separates them is that German Chamomile, sometimes known as Blue Chamomile, has a high azulene content in its chemical make-up, which accounts for the deep blue colour of the oil. The presence of this gives the oil a stronger, more soothing healing quality for some conditions than the Roman Chamomile which does not contain azulene.

Purely as a personal preference I tend to choose Roman Chamomile over the German. I find the aroma more satisfying and can almost say that it even smells as if it is healing – if that is at all possible. Roman has a lovely woody, almost almond-like aroma and is very comforting. The aroma of German Chamomile is different and more subtle, and I am not so aware of it, but, therapeutically speaking, they are both excellent oils.

Roman Chamomile, I find, is the more 'emotionally' based of the two oils. To me, it seems to 'reach the heart' very quickly and has a calming, healing effect on emotional issues that are manifesting as physical symptoms, usually connected to the stomach, but also the liver, as strong emotions can often be evidenced physically through this organ. Horses do not appear to be any different to people in this it would seem. Most horses I have dealt with prefer the Roman to the German Chamomile, but whether that is because of me and my preferences and therefore my energies being more positive when using the Roman Chamomile, it is hard to say.

Both of these oils are excellent for skin care and can be used on a wide range of allergies, cuts, inflammatory conditions, wounds, bites and sores. It is a good oil to use on youngsters that are teething (a weak solution rubbed around the jaw line as it becomes 'knobbly' is very effective and very much appreciated!).

As I mentioned earlier, Roman Chamomile works especially well on the emotions and on most stress-related complaints and anxiety-based problems. Both Roman and German Chamomile are duel-action in that they are anti-inflammatory and anti-phlogistic, affecting both the muscle and the joint and thereby being effective for relieving the aching conditions associated with arthritis and rheumatism.

Roman Chamomile is an excellent stomachic, soothing upsets and relaxing tensed muscle. If a horse has become upset and is looking 'tucked up' this is a good oil for relieving that symptom.

The Chamomiles lie in the middle to top range of cost for oils, the German being quite expensive but worth every drop for the strength of its actions. There is no need to buy more than 25ml of either oil at any one time.

As a guideline for these two oils, choose the German (blue) Chamomile for skin irritations, bites and sores and the Roman Chamomile for stress and emotional-based afflictions and rheumatic or arthritic conditions.

CITRONELLA
Cymbopogon nardus

Non-toxic, non-irritant but may cause idiosyncratic dermal sensitisation.
Extraction: steam-distilled from the grass.

I have included this oil simply on the strength of its insecticidal qualities. It is a staple of the batch of oils I keep for fly repellent use.

Most people are familiar with the smell of Citronella – it is very citrus but rather strong and I use it solely for fly repellent usage, although it has very good fungicidal and bactericidal properties also. I rarely use it alone but as an element that is part of a whole preparation.

It is not expensive and during the summer months into September, perhaps early October, I buy it in larger amounts, but rarely ever through the winter months unless we are fishing. Then it is a wonderful repellent of midges in the Tweed valley, in the closing stages of November when they can be a nightmare if the weather has not turned cold! It is worth adding to your kit during months when fly repellent is needed. In summer buy it in amounts up to 50ml.

CLARY SAGE
Salvia sclarea

No contra-indications for use noted. Do not use on pregnant mares.
Extraction: steam-distilled from the flowering tops and leaves of the herb.

This is quite a subtle aroma that reminds me of mulched leaves in autumn. It is very gentle on the nasal cavity when inhaling. I use this oil when I need to reach the deeper layers of the muscles, in which this oil seems to work very well.

It is well known for its use against throat infections and I have used it to help sooth COPD symptoms, in conjunction with Aloe Vera gel. (Gel is an easier medium than oil to work with when dealing with horses, as it will rub in more smoothly over a greater area than oil.)

Clary Sage has stomachic qualities but I personally would choose other oils first, as I tend to use it mainly for massage treatments rather than as an inhalant.

As with most oils, it has antiseptic properties, combats bacterial infections and has a gentle sedative action.

Many oils have properties which address emotional problems and Clary Sage is uplifting, sedating and relieves tension and anxiety.

Whilst it may not seem to have as many therapeutic properties as some of the other oils listed, I have included it due to its potency in massage preparations that would be used for muscular overexertion. It is not expensive and amounts up to 20ml per time are more than adequate.

EUCALYPTUS
Eucalyptus globulus (Blue Gum) or Eucalyptus radiata

If correct dosages are adhered to this is a non–irritant, non–sensitising oil.
Eucalyptus is, however, an oral toxin and should never be taken internally. It has been reported that as little as 3ml of neat Eucalyptus oil has proved fatal. Do not use with homoeopathic remedies as this oil will negate their effects.
Extraction: steam-distilled from the fresh leaves and twigs of the tree.

To me, Eucalyptus has a more 'clinical' aroma than Tea Tree, although it smells similar and there are those who think the opposite to be true. Again, the aromas differ, largely depending on your supplier. I carry two bottles, *Eucalyptus globulus* and *Eucalyptus radiata*. The *radiata* has a stronger, more powerful, aroma and is also the one I prefer to work with, although I do use the *globulus* in fly repellents with great effect.

I use Eucalyptus mainly for respiratory tract preparations as it clears the airways, sinuses and throat areas. It is also an excellent oil for use against arthritic and rheumatic conditions and overexertion injuries – although I do usually choose other oils first for these problems. This is purely personal and I would highly recommend its use for massage, especially if stimulation were required. It is a tried and tested immuno-stimulant, promoting the body's own defence mechanisms.

Eucalyptus is one you have to try before you buy. I have found that some oils are so harsh they can almost make your eyes water when you inhale. The information at the top of this profile, concerning Eucalyptus being an oral toxin, does not mean that it is dangerous just to have in the yard. Where you would use, but not drink, detergent bleach, the same applies to Eucalyptus – it simply means that the utmost care must be taken with it.

Eucalyptus is also attributed with pain-relieving qualities, is a febrifugal oil, encouraging localised circulation, causing a warming reddening effect, is a stimulant and has cytophylactic qualities – encouraging the body's own defence mechanisms against infection.

As you would expect from the aroma, this oil is also antiseptic which is why it is useful in throat and chest rubs for both humans and equines.

I have to say that it is not an oil I ever use for emotional-based issues, even though it is said to have a benefit in this area. My main use of it is as a muscle wash, a fly repellent and a throat and chest rub. Buy 10ml, or 100ml for fly repellent use.

FRANKINCENSE
Botswellia carteri

There are no contra-indications regarding use with this oil.
It is extracted via resin collected from the bark of the tree and then steam distilled.

It has to be said that you either love this oil or you hate it; there does not seem to be any middle ground. I love it and just inhaling it makes me feel as if my whole chest cavity has been filled with something warming, calming and deeply emotional. I love what I perceive to be its deep camphorous, woody smell, and it always makes me think of ancient times. Some, including horses, push it away immediately, and others quietly take in the depth of it. It does have a powerful effect upon the emotions, which is almost immediate. It has a reputation for being the 'grief' oil, and it does appear to possess an ability to distance you from deep feelings of sadness and to give a sense of detachment from it. Frankincense is an oil I am never without. It is superb for chest infections and other upper respiratory ailments and I use it in conjunction with other oils for my horse's COPD. It also works well on urinary and genital infections. Wounds, abscesses and scarring respond very well to this oil.

As I came to know more about it, I came to realise that the gift of Frankincense to Mary and the new baby Jesus was not an accident, but a well-thought-out gift of great magnitude. What is so astounding is that we are still using it today for much the same reason as it was used in biblical times. It is a relaxing, sedative oil and can be used as an antidepressant.

It is a valuable oil for use when boosting the immune system and it is one I use a lot through the winter when both humans and animals can suffer from prolonged periods of harsh weather conditions. I also use it in my mud fever preparations as it is an excellent oil for cracked and weeping skin.

On an emotional level this oil is good for apprehension, claustrophobia, fear and insecurity, panic attacks and bereavement. Bereavement can be a difficult emotion to deal with and is one that is often 'held on to', creating deep sadness. It would be a good oil to offer a horse that has just lost a much loved companion, either through death or the companion being sold on. Buy 10ml to start with.

Note: this oil is also known as Olibanum, meaning 'oil of the Lebanon' and this was the Roman name for it.

GARLIC
Allium sativum

Non-toxic, can irritate some and cause sensitisation in others.
Extraction: this oil is steam-distilled from the fresh, crushed bulbs.

This is another one of those oils that you either love or hate. Horses seem, on the whole, to be very fond of it, even the smell. Humans, on the other hand, find it too pungent in most cases.

I cannot recommend the use of this oil topically (i.e. on the skin in a massage gel or other preparation). Garlic is an excellent 'anthelmintic', which means it is an agent that dispels intestinal worms. I also use it to enhance breathing because it opens the airways and clears the sinuses. It is a good immune stimulant in that it is antiseptic, antiviral, depurative and reduces fever. Garlic is insecticidal and I use it to combat the midges that gather at certain times of the day. Always back up your use of Garlic with something soothing like German or Roman Chamomile, Yarrow or Lavender. Garlic also has larvicidal properties which is something to bear in mind when dealing with animals as they are great magnets for the nastier little bugs in life.

In too high a quotient, Garlic can cause irritation in the smooth lining of the stomach, so use Garlic granules or powder in feed as it is too easy to let more than one or two drops fall from the bottle. Garlic is also attributed with being antibiotic, bactericidal, cytophylactic, depurative, diuretic, fungicidal, hypotensive, prophylactic, sudorific and vermifugal – which explains the benefits of feeding Garlic granules with your horse's feed. Buy 10ml as only a few drops will be needed.

GERANIUM
Pelargonium graveolens

No contra-indications with this oil. Sensitive skins may be idiosyncratically affected.
Extracxtion: it is steam-distilled from the leaves, stalks and flowers of the plant.

I was pleased to reach this oil on the list as it has always been a favourite and I use it a lot. One sniff and it is summer in Provence! It has many therapeutic properties too. Some horses (and humans) find it a bit heady and they often turn away from it initially, but nearly always return to it for little 'snifters'. Geranium oil is an excellent antidepressant and deals with stress-related conditions very efficiently. It has anti-inflammatory properties, is healing, relieves tension and has an effect on the endocrine system. Geranium is one of the best natural fly repellents and is a staple ingredient of my fly repellent formulas. It works extremely well on wounds and has styptic properties, meaning that it arrests eternal bleeding (and this it does very quickly). Bruising always benefits from an application of diluted Geranium in Witch Hazel. It is also attributed with being 'anthelmintic' or 'vermifuge' which means it combats intestinal worms.

This oil is also a fungicidal agent, is an astringent, has antiseptic properties and is a good diuretic. Geranium oil is balancing to the nervous system and is hepatic in that it is a liver stimulant.

It is advised not to use this oil towards the end of the day as it has been known to cause overreaction in the brain. It is also a lymphatic stimulant, keeping the lymph system flowing and free from blockages.

On an emotional level this oil is balancing and will therefore deal with changes in temperament. It is mostly hormonally balancing so therefore brings calmness. The only drawback I find with Geranium oils is that there are so many distillations of them! Each one differs in aroma too. It is therefore a case of trial and error to find the one that suits you best. You can ask for testers – small pieces of litmus paper impregnated with the oil – so that you can smell before buying. This is a cheaper alternative to buying each variety until you find the one you feel comfortable with! I personally like Chinese Geranium which suits me and the aroma of which I find the most pleasing, thus working for me the most therapeutically. Buy 100ml for summer fly repellent use, otherwise 10–20 ml.

GINGER
Zingiber officinale

There are some notable safety aspects to be aware of with this oil. It is non-toxic, but can be an irritant if used in high doses, and it is idiosyncratically (depending on the person concerned) sensitising. It also has slightly photosensitive (reacts to sunlight) properties so it must be used with care.
Extraction: it is steam-distilled from the whole dried ground root.

I look upon this as a 'winter' oil. It has a spicy exotic aroma. Horses seem to be very partial to it. It is a stimulant and a good general tonic. It has pain-relieving qualities, is antiseptic and combats spasm. It is well known in its use for colic in humans, although I can find no data to suggest that it has been used on horses for this purpose. I have never been called upon to use it in this way. However, were that situation to arise, it would be one of the oils I would consider, along with Black Pepper, Bergamot, Peppermint, Dill and Sweet Fennel. It is attributed with excellent antispasmodic properties and this has to be of some benefit when colic-related symptoms arise. It is a good oil for nervous exhaustion. Ginger is an immune stimulant and guards against chills, fever and infectious complaints. It is also a digestive aperitif and would therefore be a good oil for horses with poor appetites. It would be a good oil to incorporate into massage gels used over joints for arthritis as it is warming, stimulating to the circulation and dispels that 'cold and damp' feeling you can sometimes get during prolonged rainy periods. It would be an ideal oil to use in a warming muscle wash after a long, hard, wet day's hunting. On the emotional level, Ginger is said to promote self-awareness and self-acceptance. Buy 10ml.

GRAPEFRUIT
Citrus paradisi

This oil has no contra-indications. Although it is a Citrus oil, it is not phototoxic but, together with its citric relatives, it does oxidise more quickly than other oils (and will therefore be deemed to be a top note).
Extraction: Grapefruit oil is extracted by cold expression from the peel of the fruit.

It has often crossed my mind that this oil is not called *Citrus paradisi* for nothing. It is a beautiful oil and most people I know love the smell of it. It is an oil high in vitamin C and is a forerunner for use against infections. It is said to be good for promoting hair growth, although I have to say I have never used it in this capacity. Grapefruit is a good oil for use in muscle preparations as it aids stiffness and fatigue and helps to disperse the lactic acid build up in muscles produced by hard exercise. It is an oil that is good for mild depression, nerves, anxiety and performance stress (good for those nervy types just before travelling or competition, etc.) Like Lemon, it has antiseptic properties and works extremely well on the lymphatic and digestive systems. Again, though, it is an oil to buy in small quantities – no more than 10-15ml at a time perhaps. It is a relatively inexpensive oil, which makes it tempting to buy it in a larger size. If you feel you would use this oil often, buy 30ml by all means but in 10ml bottles. At least then, two bottles will remain sealed and out of light until required.

Grapefruit is an excellent digestive aid due to the fact that it encourages enzymes in the stomach. It can also be used as an aperitif (aids appetite loss).

Grapefruit, like many of the other citric oils, has useful astringent properties.

On an emotional level, Grapefruit is said to help with confusion, jealousy, worry about events in the past (horses are renowned for holding on to this) frustration and indecisiveness.

IMMORTELLE
Helichrysum augustifolium

Never to be taken internally but otherwise no contra-indications.
Immortelle is also known as Helichrysum or Everlasting – which can be confusing. Extraction: steam-distilled from the everlasting flowers of the plant – hence the French have given it the name of 'Immortelle'. An absolut/concrete is also produced using solvent extractions – this looks like a deep reddish-brown paste and is not at all of a pouring consistency. It is, however, if you can get to grips with using it, absolutely fine. Most people use the distilled variety.

I really do like the smell of the absolut, though not many other people do. It smells faintly of mead – the alcoholic honey-based drink made by the monks (the best mead, as a note of interest, is to be found on Lindisfarne Island in Northumberland!) Immortelle has a lovely deep aroma and is reminiscent of the heat of summer – you can almost imagine the lazy buzz of bees as you close your eyes and inhale.

It is, however, on the expensive side, costing around £7-£10 ($4-$11) for just 2.5ml at the time of writing.

The steam-distilled variety smells slightly different and has an almost boozy, sweet mincemeat aroma.

Immortelle is very healing and soothing. It is a medium I use on bruising to very good effect. It has anti-inflammatory properties and is therefore useful against inflamed areas caused by injury.

Immortelle has antiallergenic properties and is therefore useful in skin care. I use it around cuts, abrasions, wounds and bites when, coupled with Aloe Vera gel, it is very effective. It is antiseptic, healing, combats fungal conditions, reduces body tissues (thereby eliminating retained fluids) and combats microbial activity. It is an excellent oil to use on horses that have a tendency to scrape their hock/s in the stable.

JASMINE
Jasminum officinale

Non-toxic, non-irritating, non-sensitising. Some individuals may find idiosyncratic sensitisation.
Extraction: solvent-extracted from the flowers.

To obtain a good quality oil, the flowers are harvested at night when the odour is at its peak. Unfortunately, this is not a cheap labour option and the costs are subsequently passed on in the price of the oil, making it one of the more expensive ones available. In my book, though, it is an oil that is worth every penny.

Jasmine is a lovely soothing 'euphoric' oil. It smells exotic, feels exotic and truly is. It is a wonderful oil to use for giving a calming massage to a stressed horse. It is said to have an effect on the male reproductive system and has shown some improvement when dealing with bargy stallions. Its use in massage is recommended due to its anti-inflammatory and antispasmodic effects (good for aches, pains, sprains and stiffness, etc.) Jasmine has pain-relieving qualities, is antiseptic and sedative. It also makes a good expectorant, soothing the chest.

It has to be stated clearly that this really is one of the more expensive oils, and with that in mind you will find that, even buying it in such small amounts as 10ml, it will cost you very much more than some of the more common oils you will purchase from this list. However, the point to bear in mind is that 20 drops are the equivalent of 1ml, so even if you only buy 2.5ml you will be getting 50 drops. When as little as two to three drops per time are being used, you can see that, whilst it may be expensive, it will still last for a fair period of time.

Note: *do not offer this oil to pregnant mares. Due to its parturient properties, Jasmine can cause contractions to occur.*

JUNIPER
Juniperus communis

Due to the stimulant action this oil has on the uterine muscle, it must not be used on pregnant mares or humans. It is also contra-indicated (do not use) for those with kidney complaints. There is no toxicity with this oil but a degree of irritation may be experienced by some individuals.

Extraction: steam-distilled from the needles and wood of the tree. A lesser oil with lowered therapeutic values is distilled from the berries of the tree, which have already been used to make Juniper brandy.

You may think from the above advice that this is an oil which should not appear in the home kit, but it simply means it has to be used with a degree of care and thought. This done, you will find it a valuable oil to have in your home essential oil kit.

Juniper is a very good oil for oedemic conditions, arthritis and rheumatism. I also use it on muscles after sessions of hard work, whereby it also has an effect on the joints, clearing them of any acid build-up. Stress-related problems also respond well to this oil. Juniper has antiseptic qualities, is healing, cleansing and works as a general tonic, as well as being a good stomachic. The smell of this oil reminds me of walking through damp woodland at the turn of summer into autumn. This oil is astringent and works well on the urinary system. It has excellent depurative properties and works as a good all round 'system cleanser'. Juniper has been used for hundreds of years as a ward against infection, and works very well with Rosemary to achieve this. When washing out water buckets and feed bowls, for example, a solution of warm water containing Juniper works as an efficient tool against possible infection and bacterial residues. It is a useful oil to use against fleas and ticks. Whilst Juniper is renowned for clearing waste from the body, it works just as well on clearing over-stimulated minds. I see no reason for this not to work as well on horses as it does on humans. The dilution for this should be very weak, as it should for any treatment around the head.

On an emotional level, Juniper is said to be good for combating lethargy. Buy 20ml.

Note: *Juniper is a highly mobile oil and will come out of the bottle very fast. Be prepared for this when measuring out your drops.*

LAVENDER
Lavandula officinalis

No contra-indications with this oil.
Extraction: steam-distilled from the fresh flowering tops of the plant.

Lavender, it would seem, is the essential oil world's panacea for all ills. It would be easier to list what it does not do, rather than what it does do. Strangely enough, I am not that keen on the smell of this oil – I find it can be a bit cloying. English Lavender can be very expensive and I know of one company which distils its crops of English Lavender for seven seasons before releasing it for sale. It has to be said that it is a very high quality oil, but I personally prefer the French Lavender, as I find it lighter and 'thinner' in its essence than the heavier English variety. Personal preferences aside, no essential oil kit should ever be without this oil, under any circumstances! If you have no other oil but this one, you would still be able to cover a wide range of presenting problems. Wound management would certainly benefit from this oil. It is high in linalyl acetate (the French variety often more so than the English) and this is what gives the oil its soothing cicatrizant (healing) action. It is one of the very few oils that can be used undiluted. However, just because it can be does not mean to say it *should* be and I would recommend that you *always* dilute the essential oil no matter what.

Lavender is a natural fly repellent and should be well utilised for this. Buying a cheaper brand, whereby you may get more oil for your money as it is 'only going into a fly repellent mix', is false economy. It will be less effective (I know for I have tried) and you will have to use more oil, so in the end nothing will have been gained. Therefore it is prudent, as with all the oils you buy, always to buy the very best oil you can afford.

Lavender has renowned antiseptic properties (making it good for wound management), pain-relieving qualities, is sedative, calming and soothing. It is also an excellent antispasmodic, has very high bactericidal effects and can be used as a decongestant.

Lavender is also attributed as being cytophylactic, which means it is an oil that encourages cellular renewal processes within the body, thereby aiding the body to heal itself. Used as an antidepressant the effects can be very quick to lift the spirits and clear the head. What has to be borne in mind with Lavender, however, is that whilst it is a sedative when used correctly, if too much exposure to the oil is experienced, or it is used in too strong a dose, it can have the opposite effect, causing headaches and wakefulness and sometimes restlessness.

When Lavender is used on the respiratory system of the body it is able to help such conditions as sinusitis, asthma and bronchial problems and is an excellent agent for the prevention of infectious conditions that would affect this tract.

Mixed with Arnica (carrier) oil, it is a very useful combatant of rheumatic conditions.

Preparations it can be added to include those for combating ticks and parasites, lice, ringworm, spots, bites, abscesses and most dermatological problems, inflammatory situations regarding skin and muscles, stomachic conditions that need soothing and promotion of the general health of the liver. It is also an excellent antitoxic oil.

This is a true one-man show which suits nearly all horse breeds and personality types Frequent usage. Buy 50ml.

LEMON
Citrus limonum

This oil is photo-toxic. Do not use if exposing skin to direct sunlight, including the skin of your horse, especially if it is a grey. Lemon can also cause dermal irritation and sensitisation if used in too strong a dose.
Extraction: by cold expression from the fresh rind of the fruit.

Despite having to treat this oil with care, it is one I love, and I find most other people do too. There is something very clean and very refreshing about it – it even smells cleansing (as do Lime, Orange Grapefruit, etc.).

I tend to use more of this oil in the spring and summer, strangely enough, and much less in winter. It is a lovely oil, although it can differ from supplier to supplier, so search for one that *feels* right for you when you inhale it.

Lemon has many therapeutic properties and is excellent for getting the circulation going. It is also one of those oils that is hyper- or hypo-tensive – meaning it is a regulatory oil, either up or down accordingly. (That is, it will bring temperature down if it is up, and will bring temperature up if it has dropped.) It is said to be good for blood pressure because of that regulating feature.

Due to its citric properties, it is good against acidic conditions such as arthritis and rheumatism. It is a good astringent on the tissues of the body. It is certainly a good antitoxin agent and so very good for depurative uses. Lemon is also one of the better bactericidal agents. It is an insecticide and so is always a staple ingredient of any fly repellents I may make up. Lemon is one of those oils that just do so much: it helps promote sweating, which rids the body of toxins, it is antiseptic and so is good for use around cuts and wounds (always use it diluted, remembering that this oil can be sensitising in too high a dosage). It has healing properties, relieves muscular spasm, reduces temperature and fever and encourages production of the all important white blood cells.

Do treat this oil with care, though. Do not leave it in direct sunlight and never leave the top off the bottle as Citrus oils oxidise quicker than other oils and an oxidised oil can cause irritation and sensitisation. Work on the premise of a six-month shelf life for Citrus oils once they have been opened, longer if not.

A similar oil to Lemon is Lime, which is equally refreshing and almost as good. Lemon is regarded as a top note oil, meaning its volatility rate is high.

Lemon also has mild styptic (stems external bleeding) properties. It is an excellent carminative, reducing stomachic bloating very quickly.

Frankincense and Lemon are very good together. Mix Lemon with lower noted oils, the sharpness of the Lemon will help alleviate the headiness of some of the heavier oils. Lemon and Chamomile are good for maintaining immunity against infectious illnesses and viruses. Buy in 10-15ml quantities because of its short shelf life.

MYRRH
Commiphora myrrha

Toxic in concentrated amounts, otherwise no contra-indications.
Extraction: a resinoid is collected by using solvent-extraction, and the leaves of the shrub are also steam-distilled.

This is another oil that I adore and which belongs to my stable of 'winter oils'. The aroma of Myrrh is similar to that of Patchouli in that it is deeply warming and has great substance. (Opoponax is another oil similar to Myrrh.) This is another oil that I use in wound management, its other main use being for respiratory tract ailments.

I use Myrrh in skin preparations, especially where the threat of microbial infection may be present. Myrrh is antiphlogistic and therefore a good combatant against arthritic conditions, helping to soothe and calm complaints of the chest (good for horses with a wide-ranging COPD problem).

I have also used this oil with good effect as a styptic agent, and to this end I always keep a pot of Aloe Vera gel containing this oil as part of our yard first aid kit.

Myrrh can be quite expensive, but I find it worth every penny as it is so effective. Buy in quantities of up to 20ml at a time.

PALMAROSA
Cymbopogon martini

No contra-indications.

Extraction: steam-distillation of the grass.

This is another lovely oil which I buy purely for its beneficial effects on the skin of both human and equine. It has a lovely fresh citrus smell something like a cross between Lemongrass and Geranium.

It does not have a vast list of therapeutic values but its use in skin care is so good that it is worth having just for that purpose alone. Use it for infected skin, over wounds that are not quite healing as quickly as they should, over sores, spots, bites – very aspect of skin care will benefit from an application. It has a hydrating, moisturising effect on the skin and is good teamed with Patchouli when mud fever sores are beginning to heal. It has bactericidal properties and is antiseptic, both requirements for healing wounds/skin disorders.

It is a circulatory stimulant, thus promoting the carriage of nutrients around the body, which, in turn, promotes healing processes.

It will soon clear the condition if used in a cold cream base as a moisturiser on cracked heels at the healing stage.

It is not expensive but 20ml at any one time is a sufficient quantity to buy in.

PATCHOULI
Pogestemon cablin

No contra-indications.

Extraction: steam-distilled from the dried leaves of the herb.

I do love this oil; it reminds me of my childhood when there was a certain cough linctus on the market and Patchouli smells just like it. It is a wonderfully camphorous oil with hints of Eastern cultures about it, a sense of antiquity in its deep resonant aroma.

I use it specifically for skin care with absolutely amazing results. It has never let me down. Cuts, bruises, wounds, bites, open sores, skin infections – all have benefited from Patchouli being applied. I find, for me, that Patchouli and Myrrh blended together make an excellent wound management solution. Occasionally I use it in an insect repellent but mostly I keep it for use on skin complaints. It is wonderful when used to combat mud fever. On applying to my gelding last winter over fairly severe mud fever, hair was growing back seven days after the first application to the cracked, sore skin.

Patchouli is an anti-inflammatory agent. It is also antiphlogistic and thus good for use against arthritis and rheumatism. Like most oils it possesses antiseptic qualities, whilst also combating fungal invasions. It promotes the body's own defence mechanisms to function more fully and rids the body of toxins, microbial influences and viral conditions.

You will not use much of this oil, so a quantity of up to 25ml is sufficient to keep at any one time. Unlike other oils, Patchouli is regarded as the one oil that seems to mature with age without any detriment to its efficacy.

PEPPERMINT
Mentha piperita

Possible sensitisation in individual cases. Otherwise non-toxic and non-irritant. This is not an oil to use in concentration due to its strength. Has been known to negate homoeopathic remedies being taken due to the strength of the oil.
Extraction: steam-distilled from the fresh leaves of the plant when in flower.

Who could fail to like this oil? I use copious amounts of it for just about everything. It has a fresh, zingy smell that is emotive of spring and early summer. It is crisp and clean smelling and is universally liked by both human and equine. Just like Lavender, there are many attributable properties connected with this oil. I use it for respiratory tract problems, for pain relief, muscular spasms, stimulation of the circulation, for arthritic and rheumatic conditions and absolutely without fail on aches and sprains, muscle and tendon problems and for extreme physical and mental fatigue.

Unusually, Peppermint is possessed of 'hot and cold' properties and is therefore extremely useful when combating pain relief or the acidic conditions of inflamed joints and muscles associated with arthritis and rheumatism. When used on an emotional level Peppermint clears the head and assists mental fatigue and nervous conditions. It is generally an all round system booster and one I would never be without.

Peppermint is also considered to be one of the best and most natural stomachics available to us, being able to assist with a wide range of problems relating to the digestive system.

Other therapeutic properties for this oil are that it is antiseptic, hepatic (beneficial to the liver), promotes sweating, thereby eliminating toxins, and is useful against intestinal worms.

It must be noted, however, that due to the strength of this oil it cannot be taken in conjunction with homoeopathic remedies as it will negate their effects.

There are numerous types of Peppermint. I particularly like Peppermint USA. It is a case of trying them and seeing which oil you identify with most. Buy 20–100ml depending on frequency of usage.

PINE
Pinus sylvestris

Idiosyncratic sensitisation may be experienced and high levels of oil to carrier may cause skin irritation.
Extraction: a different process is used to extract this oil from the needles, which is still a form of distillation but does not use steam.

I have to admit that whilst I personally like the aroma of this oil, it is fair to say that the odour is rather clinical and reminiscent of a hospital ('disinfectant', as someone said when inhaling it for their opinion of its aroma!). It is not the prettiest, sweetest or most attractive of aromas, but it does have extensive therapeutic properties and, at the end of the day, it is this that matters most. I do feel that the term 'aromatherapy' often has a lot to answer for in that many people expect everything to smell sweet, lovely and wonderful. Well, in truth it does not. One could almost adapt the old adage of 'if it tastes nice it isn't doing you any good' to cover some of the aromas of essential oils. The ones that possess the most therapeutic value do tend to be the ones with the less 'pretty' aromas!

There is a vast range of therapeutic uses for Pine oil. I use it mostly for respiratory conditions due to its antiseptic, bactericidal, balsamic (soothing to the chest) and expectorant (dispels mucus) properties. When blended with other oils it is an extremely useful oil for combating many aspects of COPD and alleviating the symptoms of that broad-based problem. I also use it extensively as a fly repellent for which it is very effective.

Pine has a beneficial effect upon the liver, combats intestinal worms, dispels build up of fluid in the body, is a circulatory stimulant and is another oil which combats the acidic conditions of arthritis and rheumatism. Whilst it is attributed with assisting in stress-related conditions, I have to say I do not use it for this, preferring Yarrow, Rose, Benzoin, Frankincense and Violet Leaf, amongst others, for this purpose. This is purely a personal choice.

Pine is not expensive but buying large amounts simply because of that is false economy. Buy in quantities of up to 25ml in winter and up to 100ml if to be used as a fly repellent in the summer.

ROSE
Cabbage Rose – *Rosa centifolia*
Damask Rose – *Rosa damascena*

This is another pair of oils, like the Chamomiles, that I find simply impossible to separate and I will therefore describe them in tandem. Both are free of contra-indications in that neither is toxic, sensitising nor an irritant, although some sensitisation has been noted in certain horses.
Extraction: both steam distillation and solvent extraction are used to obtain the oil from the petals.

These oils are very much associated with emotional states. During the time preceding editing of this book, I would have said, quite categorically, that I hated these two oils. Whilst I acknowledged the long list of therapeutic properties of the oils, I personally could not bear to use them or have them in my main box! I would even 'dispense' with gifts of cosmetics and bubble baths etc. that contained even a trace of this aroma. I would, of course, have included a resumé of the oils, despite my misgivings about them, simply because they are so very good. However, in the intervening period I have used them for myself, on the advice of another therapist, and have to say that I now like the aroma, even if it is not one of my favourites. Rose would therefore be good for any horse holding on to emotional issues of a longstanding nature. It is gentle on the emotions, whilst easing them at the same time.

Rose oil is *extremely* expensive. The amount of petals needed is vast compared to the yield. For example, at the time of writing, you could expect to pay somewhere between £16–£27 ($20–$25) for just 2.5ml.

71

The absolut is slightly cheaper, but still expensive. It is also one of those oils that you must obtain a tester for as they differ so much from batch to batch. I have found that a lot of Rose oils are too sweet and cloying and can sit on the back of the throat so that you continue smelling/tasting them for hours afterwards.

If you find a Rose oil that is not expensive and you think that you have found a bargain, the oil is almost certainly adulterated. A good Rose oil aroma should have no quick, sharp edges to it, but be deep and rounded, sweet without being sickly. Choose carefully and use it carefully too. As I mentioned above, Rose is one of the more emotionally based oils and it is very easy to promote a 'healing crisis' with it as it releases emotions and opens up the psyche. I used to be prone to tears when using Rose oil – however, my own emotional neuroses and dysfunctions are for another four-volume publication and not suitable here in a book about horses!

Rose oil has many properties and can be used for so many things. It is renowned as the female hormone balancer as it acts as a stimulant on the adrenal cortex of the endocrine system. It has regulating and cleansing effects on the liver, promotes general health and well-being and is a good immuno-stimulant. It will benefit the respiratory system and can also be used against rheumatism and muscular sprain.

On an emotional level it calms and eases stress and tension, fatigue caused by nervous anxiety is lessened, it is restorative and releases emotions that are being 'held on to'.

Rose has pain-relieving qualities, combats microbial invasion, disperses oxidants in the body and can be used for wounds, cuts, etc. due to its antiseptic, fungicidal and vulnerary properties. It clears the head and promotes clear thinking. It is healing in that it promotes leucocyte production in the body to combat infection. This oil is rubefacient (locally warming) for use in massage, encouraging blood flow and the carrying of nutrients around the body. It promotes sweating, thereby eliminating toxins. It is also a good stomachic and an all round general tonic.

Rose is also a good oil to use for eye infections. Use two drops of oil in a tea cup of water hot enough to dissolve the oil but not too hot to use. Soak a square of cotton wool in the solution and bathe over the eye. Use the solution until it cools and the oil begins to form again in the water. I used this recently on a horse who was bitten on the upper eyelid. The eye was completely puffy and swollen and he could not open it at all. Twenty minutes after bathing the eye with the above solution, a reduction in the swelling was obvious. Within three hours the eye was virtually back to normal and the horse comfortable again. The horse also fell asleep whilst the bathing process was taking place so there had to be something acceptable about the procedure considering the sensitive area that was being worked on!

Rose oil *is* expensive and will cost you anything from about £1.00 ($2) per drop for all that therapeutic benefit. It is, however, worth it and is an oil that should have a place in any aromatherapy kit.

ROSEMARY
Rosmarinus officinalis

No contra-indications. Do not use on pregnant mares or if high blood pressure is present.
Extraction: steam-distilled using the fresh flowering heads of the plant.

This is another oil I try never to be without, so extensive is its therapeutic usage.

Rosemary has a strong aroma which, if used in great strength, will cause headaches, so take care to dilute it well. That said, the aroma of this oil is quite lovely, with a fresh smell somewhat along the lines of Peppermint. I cannot, however, stop my stomach lurching in anticipation each time I use this oil. Within seconds my taste buds are watering and, try as I might to banish them, visions of roast lamb sally forth regardless!

This oil has so many therapeutic properties it is hard to know where to begin. I am never without it during the summer months as I use it extensively in fly repellent mixes with great effect. It is also an efficient oil against lice should they be experienced (especially in manes and tails that have been matted for some time). Rosemary is a circulatory stimulant and is therefore a good agent when combating water retention, sluggish circulations whereby a build up of toxins is occurring and in preparations for use against rheumatism. It is a powerful oil for use in problems of the respiratory tract and it blends well with Lavender for this as Lavender seems to bring a gentleness to the blend.

This oil is one of the main immuno-stimulants and promotes general health and well-being.

On an emotional level it is said to help aid concentration, combat mental fatigue by clearing the head and to relieve conditions brought about by nervous dispositions. Like many oils it has antiseptic properties and is also hepatic, aiding the general health of the liver. It is an able tonic, stomachic and eliminator of toxins through its sudorific property (promotes sweating). Rosemary has mild pain-relieving qualities and is a preventive agent against the build up of microbial infections in the body. When used in a massage preparation it has excellent rubefacient qualities, increasing the localised circulation of the blood and warming the muscles. It is not one of the more expensive oils and it is therefore false economy to buy it cheaply when the very best oils are not that much more expensive. Quality is everything. Buy in amounts up to 25ml, which should be sufficient, unless you are intending to use this throughout the summer in fly repellents when perhaps you would need to buy more.

ROSEWOOD
Aniba rosaeodora var *amizonica ducke*

No contra-indications noted with this oil.
Extraction: steam-distilled from the wood of the Rosewood Tree.

This is a lovely oil. It has a deep, warm smell, emotive of Eastern cultures. It is not vast in its range of therapeutic values but I am often drawn to it for its cephalic qualities. It is a fine oil to use in promoting the immune system, combating as it does infectious invasions and feverish conditions. It is a prime oil for skin care as it is gentle and soothing. I use it on wound sites that have almost healed but are left as a bare patch of scaly dry skin (e.g. after a bad insect bite that has begun to heal, or where a horse has been bitten by another horse and the stage has been reached where the skin is drying and needs something keep it from drying out completely).

It softens the skin and keeps it supple and moist, preventing any scaliness caused by the elements and poor healing. The carrier I use in this instance is Linseed oil, sometimes with a small amount of Aloe Vera gel added. Rosewood is an antidepressant and will invoke deep sighs if offered for inhaling – and not just from our four-legged friends either!

I particularly like this oil for skin care management because of its antiseptic, antimicrobial and bactericidal properties, and I have sometimes used it in sweet itch preparations to good effect. It is a general tonic and works well when added to massage blends.

It is not expensive but there is no need to buy more than 10ml at a time.

SANDALWOOD
Santalum album

This is another virtually vice-free oil. As with all oils, used inappropriately it could cause idiosyncratic irritation.

Extraction: steam-distilled from the inner wood of the tree once the outer layers have been consumed by ants! It is important to understand the oil you are ordering and ask for it by its Latin name as well as its common name. This is because there are alternative varieties from other continents (i.e. Australia) which do not have the therapeutic properties of the above named oil.

This is a lovely woody-smelling oil and very penetrating. Inhaling this oil has an effect in the chest very quickly. Sandalwood is a wonderful oil for the respiratory system, especially for chest complaints, dry coughing and bronchial problems. It is an uplifting oil and can be used for depressive conditions. I use this oil when massaging after prolonged exertion as it is 'antiphlogistic' and therefore has an effect on the joints as well as the muscles. This is a good oil for use in arthritic and rheumatic conditions. It has insecticidal properties and is one of the list of oils I use in fly repellent preparations. This oil combats bacterial conditions. In ancient times it was used to combat urinary tract infections. Sandalwood is one of the few oils that can be used for eye infections. Use one drop in a tea cup of water that is warm but not hot. Soak a square cotton pad in the solution, press most of the water out and bathe over the infected area. Repeat until the water begins to cool and the oil begins to form again.

Sandalwood is also attributed with astringent properties, with being antispasmodic, bactericidal, carminative, fungicidal, an expectorant and a good all round general tonic.

On a psychological level Sandalwood is attributed with assisting with fear-related conditions, insecurity, irritability and sensitivity. Buy 10ml at a time.

SWEET MARJORAM
Origanum marjorana

No contra-indications noted with this oil other than it cannot be used on pregnant mares (or humans).

Extraction: steam distillation of the flowering tops of the plant, which have first been picked and dried.

This is another oil with very deep and warm tones to it and with a hint of the orient about it. I use it in massage because of this warmth, and for its anti-oxidant properties. It is very cleansing. All muscular and joint problems benefit from this oil, especially stiffness caused through wet, cold (i.e. after hunting perhaps) and overexertion, and especially all three of those elements together.

Marjoram is an excellent oil for use against ticks (blend with Aloe and Seaweed gel for application). I have also used this on dogs – who do not seem to like it very much no matter how good it may be! (Apply with a cotton bud, especially for ticks on dogs as the body area of the tick is so small.)

Whilst Marjoram has beneficial uses for the respiratory tract, I tend to choose other oils for this area first before choosing Marjoram. If, however, it would seem that a chill might be taking effect it is an excellent oil to use. Marjoram has laxative properties, so you may see a difference in the horse's droppings whilst using this oil.

Other properties attributed to Marjoram are bactericidal, antiseptic and fungicidal effects – three good results when promoting general health and well-being.

Marjoram has a sedative effect on the nervous system and will calm and ease anxiety.

Buy in amounts of 10–25ml.

TAGETES
Tagetes minuta

This oil can cause dermal irritation and sensitisation if not handled with due care.

Extraction: mostly steam-distilled when the herb is in full flower, but a small amount of absolut is produced by solvent extraction.

You may wonder why I would include an oil that you have to be so careful with and which is so strong. I do so because I like it and because when used to combat microbial infection it is extremely good. It is a good sedative, promotes cellular renewal in healing wounds and is fungicidal.

It is a broncho-dilatory oil and I often add it to respiratory lotions that will be massaged in over the chest and throat.

I rarely use it alone but as part of a blend. I like its energies and whilst it is not quite a mainstream oil, for those of you wishing to progress beyond the simpler, easier oils, this is a good one to try.

It is not expensive and 10-20ml at a time is more than sufficient.

TEA TREE
Malaleuca alternifolia

Idiosyncratic reaction in some, otherwise no contra-indications. Do not use this oil on dogs at all as it has been known to cause temporary paralysis.
Extraction: steam-distilled from the leaves and twigs of the tree.

Whether you like the smell of this oil or not, it is one that I recommend that you never run out of. Between this oil and Lavender, you would have most eventualities catered for! It is not what I would call a pretty aroma by any means. In fact it is very clinical and does smell like something you would expect to find in a first aid kit. It is the world's most natural antibiotic and it is invaluable.

With regard to the aroma, it has to be said that this differs enormously from supplier to supplier. I currently have three bottles of this oil in my kit, all from different suppliers and all of them attributed as *Malaleuca alternifolia* but only one has any real substance to its aroma. The one that does have 'body' to it, interestingly enough, is a bottle my husband brought back for me from Australia. Why this should smell so different and, in tests, be preferred by everyone I offered the three bottles to, I cannot say! They are all from the same plant after all. It is one of the vagaries of essential oil therapy. 'Sniff around', find the oil that suits you and your energy best. The one purchased for me in Australia not only simply smells the best but feels as if it has more 'energy' to it – a phenomenon I cannot explain.

Tea Tree can be used for so many things: cuts, wounds, grazes, sores, bites, as an insect repellent, infections (including wounds that have become septic), thrush and infectious illnesses. Thankfully I have never had, or come across, a case of strangles, but I would reach for this oil without hesitation if I did.

This oil is also a staple in all the respiratory preparations I use as it combats bronchial problems that involve airborne bacteria better than any oil I know. Tea Tree also has balsamic properties which will soothe and ease congestion in the chest. It is a powerful immuno-stimulant, encouraging the natural defences of the body and inhibiting viral, fungicidal and bacterial activity.

Tea Tree has been used in Australia by the native Australian population for hundreds of years. It is not expensive and during the summer months I would buy larger quantities (up to 100ml at a time), than in the winter, when fly repellents are not really needed.

If I were asked if this is a popular oil with horses, in all honesty, I would have to say no. It is not one of the oils that they would come back to smell again after an initial inhalation. However, they do not object to it being used in preparations and it is extremely good at its job. So, smell, at the end of the day, is not everything. A view that not all people who use essential oils would agree with.

VETIVER
Vetiveria zizanoides

Non-toxic, non-irritant, non-sensitising.
Extraction: steam-distilled from the roots which have been prepared, dried and then soaked.

As far as aromas go, I cannot honestly say that this is a pretty one. It is very earthy, which is interesting considering that this is an oil I would choose if I felt a horse needed 'grounding' emotionally. It is also a bit moth-ballish too and has a damp, woody feel to it – very much an autumn smell. That said, I do like it very much. To me it smells deep and as if it has great substance. I use this mainly on the emotional level as it is so good for stress-related conditions, including nervous tension. It is very relaxing and grounding, as I have mentioned above. Horses being the emotional creatures they are, I find this oil of great assistance. It does have other uses, mainly for arthritis, rheumatism and aches, pains and sprains. I would also use this as a constituent of a muscle wash preparation. It can be used around cuts and wounds as it has enormous antiseptic properties and is a cell stimulator, promoting healing. It is also a good oil against intestinal worms. I have recommended this oil simply on the strength of its 'grounding' abilities. Due to its deeply relaxing qualities it is a useful oil to use in situations where horses are being bargy and unpredictable or need settling into a new stable/home/yard. It is not expensive and so makes a good staple for your home kit. 10ml per purchase would be enough.

VIOLET LEAF
Viola odorata

There are no contra-indications with this oil except to warn that in some individuals some sensitisation may be experienced.
Extraction: solvent-extracted from the fresh leaves and flowers of the plant. This oil contains salicylic acid which is the basis of aspirin, so use it with care, especially on competition horses.

This is another oil that I consider to have a 'winter' personality – although someone else I know felt it was the heat of summer when everywhere is hot, heady and heavy, which best described it. As you can see, our sense of smell is quite emotive and different. This is interesting, as Sweet Violet (*Viola odorata*) is considered a spring flower and scent by garden experts. Once again, it comes down to personal opinion.

For me, this is another deep-smelling oil which has a musty, mulched-leaves feel to it. Some oils have clearer undertones and it is these that I personally prefer. There are three oils that, for me, group together to provide the same kind of function – these are Vetiver, Violet Leaf and Valerian. They are all what is termed 'emotionally based' oils which have therapeutic properties in the rheumatic, aching, and relaxing areas. As with the other two oils, Violet Leaf can be used around wounds due to its mild pain-relieving qualities.

This oil has been found to have a beneficial effect on the liver, which again harks back to the emotional side, as the emotions can be 'held' in the liver and manifest themselves as a physical symptom. This oil also helps to dispel toxins. It is a good oil to choose if a horse has just come to a new yard and is feeling the move rather keenly, if nervous exhaustion has taken a physical toll, say, after bonfire night when some horses can work themselves into an emotional lather about what seems a very real but unseen threat. If horses are clip-shy, try keeping a weak solution to hand for the horse to inhale and to calm it down. It is an oil that is said to comfort the heart. I am never without the three oils, Violet Leaf, Vetiver and Valerian, and am then covered for most emotional issues.

Unfortunately, this oil is not one of the cheaper ones and is extremely expensive for even a small amount – you will not get much change out of £15 ($12) for 2.5ml of it at the time of writing! However, it is worth bearing in mind that 2.5ml is 50 drops and so, perhaps, it is worth experimenting with for at least one bottle's worth!

YARROW
Achillea millefolium

No adverse contra-indications, although there are some who may have a reaction against it, especially on the emotional level. On the whole, though, a safe oil.
Extraction: it is steam-distilled from the picked, dried herb.

I have had some very adverse reactions to this oil from humans. They have sworn blind that they *know* it kills horses but I am not aware of there ever having been a recorded occurrence of that fact. It is worth pointing out, however, that different parts of a plant do different things. How many people know that rhubarb leaves are poisonous to humans, but we eat the stems with impunity? I fear the same has to be said for this oil. Boil up the roots into an infusion and you could well be asking for trouble as it *could* be poisonous (as told to me by someone who regarded me as the harbinger of death for even possessing a bottle of this oil, let alone using it around horses!). However, the essential oil of Yarrow, distilled from the dried herb, does not pose that problem. That said, it can be a 'tricky' oil. One of its uses is for emotional problems. Normally this is when an emotional trauma has caused the manifestation of a physical problem, or when the problem is being held on to, which often happens with emotional trauma – we simply forget to let go. Horses are no different in this respect. Yarrow is excellent for helping a horse to let go emotionally of any trauma it has experienced, real or otherwise. It is vitally important not to overload the horse with this oil. Use it with extreme care and in a dilution of 1:5ml.

The other uses for Yarrow are on allergies, bites and wounds. Yarrow contains azulene and is therefore soothing. It is very good on sensitive areas of skin (use in a gel not in a carrier oil for horses). It is also good for kidney or bladder infections which always respond well to this oil. Yarrow is a good constituent of sweet itch preparations and on the jaw line (again in a gel carrier not an oil) after equine dental work has been carried out. Yarrow, along with oils such as German or Blue Chamomile and Lavender, will soften the harsher effects of Garlic.

Yarrow has excellent anti-inflammatory properties and is therefore good for relieving cramp-type symptoms. It is a circulatory stimulant and can aid digestion because it soothes the smooth muscle of the stomach.

On an emotional level Yarrow is said to combat negative feelings, distancing the receiver of the oil from negative and draining influences. It is therefore a good oil for a horse who has lost confidence in itself and no longer trusts in its own abilities.

Once again, this is not a cheap oil. At the time of writing £15 would buy you 5ml. However, when you consider that 5ml is 100 drops, and that you would only ever be using 1-3 drops at any one time, 5ml will last you quite a while. To buy a larger quantity would simply be false economy. I have found this difficult to source in USA.

YLANG YLANG
Cananga odorata

There are no contra-indications with this oil. However, it has a heady aroma which can cause headaches and feelings of nausea if an individual (horse or human) is exposed to too low a dilution or for prolonged periods of time.

Extraction: a complex series of events is attached to this oil. It is steam-distilled from the fresh flowers of the plant but can be distilled up to four times. This gives four different distillations of the same oil. Ylang Ylang Extra is the most expensive of the four distillations and is obviously the first one. Ylang Ylang I, II and III are obviously lesser oils than the Extra version, but still extremely good. They are also less expensive than one would imagine them to be. The 'Extra' distillation is really not that much more expensive than the I-III distillations, so my recommendation would be to go for the very best you can afford or feel is right for you. Remember, quality is everything!

Ylang Ylang – which I was taught to pronounce with a back-of-the-throat 'L', but which others pronounce eelang eelang – is a beautiful oil and one of my personal favourites, therefore I use it a lot. Whether it works so well because I love it so much and thoroughly enjoy using it, or whether it is because it really is a very good oil on its own – who can say? That said, Ylang Ylang is not to everyone's taste. It is headily deep and exotic, but also very slightly cloying, which is what will cause some individuals to suffer headaches.

I often use this in a massage gel for a horse who needs 'picking up' and to be made to feel that all is well with the world again. It is a deeply relaxing, very soothing oil. I use it on my mare in a head massage. It also promotes hair growth, soothes irritated patches of skin and can be used on insect bites.

I do not think this to be an expensive oil. It walks the middle ground. Buy in quantities of up to 10ml at any one time.

Salicylic Acid

I am going to take a moment to mention this chemical component here rather than in the botanical chemistry section. This is because knowing what little I do of human nature, it is quite possible that most people will skip the 'chemistry' bit in the relevant chapter.

A few of you might have heard of this chemical constituent through the media cover of the Coral Cove debacle (the horse that belonged to and was ridden by the late Polly Phillips).

I mention it here because it is a substance which occurs naturally in the chemical make-up of certain plants and, by association, some essential oils (Sweet Birch, *Cananga odorata*/Ylang Ylang, Wintergreen, Violet Leaf among others). Salicylic acid is the building block from which aspirin is manufactured.

Competition horses are permitted a certain level of salicylic acid in their system at any one time (usually given by injection of aspirin for an injury). I think attention must be drawn to the fact that some essential oils do contain this element.

There have been no recorded instances of a horse being over the permitted limit due to the use of complementary products. However, until scientific tests are run, it is impossible to say whether prolonged use of any of the above oils will not cause a build up in the system of salicylic acid, and that, should the horse be given an injection, it would be enough to send levels over the limit. This is purely a personal point of view, but one I think it only prudent to bear in mind. If you do own a competition horse, of whatever discipline, and there has been long-term use of a preparation containing the above mentioned oils, perhaps for a tendon strain or muscular condition, then I think it important that this information is borne in mind. Preparations bought over the counter tend not to be too strong in the elements they contain, say, for instance, a lotion for a muscle strain that may contain Sweet Birch. However, if your horse is being seen by a therapist using oils, it has to be borne in mind how concentrated these oils are and that therefore the levels of these elements may be somewhat higher.

Hydrolats
What they are and when to use them

Hydrolats are an important part of essential oil usage. They are also known as 'flower waters' and are a by-product of the steam distillation process. Steam forced through the plant material under gentle pressure is siphoned off, sent through a cooler which turns it back into a liquid and is then stored in a second vat. The essential oil sits on the top of this liquid and is skimmed off. What is left is the hydrolat or flower water.

In the main, hydrolats have been largely ignored for a long time and even now not many people use them as extensively as they could. I am a great believer in them and have half a dozen in use at any one time. I have heard people argue that if they are a by-product, what use can they be? That is the very point. Because they are a by-product, all the therapeutic values attached to an essential oil must have left their traces in the hydrolat. They are an invaluable part of the essential oil kit.

To all intents and purposes they look like clear water and, in fact, some have very little odour to them. However, they can be used in many ways.

When making up a solution for strained muscles and tendons I use Lavender water to 'let down' the Aloe Vera gel. I use Lavender water and Lemon water in fly repellents. If 200ml of liquid is required I use 100ml of ionised water and 100ml of hydrolat. Rose water is an excellent eyewash. Juniper water also goes into massage 'aches and sprains' solutions. Witch Hazel hydrolat is good for bruising, as is Geranium hydrolat. The Chamomile hydrolats are used for soothing, skin rashes, minor bruising and knocks and on bites and stings. I use Lavender hydrolat for washing manes and tails, added to a bowl of water. The hydrolats are soothing and calming, gentle and kind, and suit most skin types.

The hydrolats available include those listed below.

Witch Hazel	**Chamomile**	**Jasmine**
Lavender	**Orange Rose**	**Ylang Ylang**
Cornflower	**Eucalyptus**	**Fir Silver**
Juniper	**Linden Blossom**	**Marigold**
Melissa	**Orange Blossom**	**Peppermint**
Pine	**Rose Otto**	**Sage**
Verbena		

These hydrolats are nearly always certified 'organic' by the companies selling them and are considered to be 100 per cent natural products with no contra-indications. Most companies will state that they are microbiologically tested. The recommended shelf life is between 9-12 months, less if opened. In the chapter on blending you will see them as part of the ingredients of all manner of solutions, creams and gels.

I would recommend buying them in 100ml quantities at a time until you know what you will use each one for and how much you will want to add to the blend. In USA hydrolats are sold in 4floz or 8floz quantities. Suppliers will quote for larger amounts.

CHAPTER 6

Chemical Phytotomy

The Organic Chemistry of Essential Oils

It is almost a certainty that all of you reading this will have heard of the expression 'a necessary evil'. This chapter happens to be one of them.

Organic chemistry is complicated, cannot be said to be easy to understand, and is littered with words almost impossible to pronounce. However, essential oils are part of the process of organic chemistry. Therefore, it is important that a basic knowledge, if not an understanding, is acquired. Some of you reading this book may decide that you would like to become essential oil therapists – aromatherapists – and will embark upon formal training. Underpinning that whole training will be the organic chemistry of essential oils, in which you will be immersed in great detail. This, however, is not a training manual for would-be therapists. Ergo, it is slightly difficult to decide to what level to take this subject within the confines of this guidebook.

Organic chemistry can consist of great tracts of text which, although written in English, actually appear to be a completely foreign language. Few of the therapists I trained with actually enjoyed the subject and most laboured through it dutifully. Which still leaves the question of how to approach the subject within the confines of this book.

I know from experience that, when faced with great tracts of text, after a while the words begin to swim on the page, I begin to fidget, I skip paragraphs, hoping that my eye will catch a word that will prove to be important and that I will have absorbed at least *something* whilst I surfed the pages! It is a common enough phenomenon and one I would like to try to avoid here. Despite everything I have said, at a certain level organic chemistry is absolutely fascinating. It teaches us that Mother Nature is indeed a truly wondrous thing. It teaches us that essential oils are definitely not just innocuous substances in little bottles, which smell nice. The decision I have taken is to present a broad-based outline of the subject, covering the main constituents, so that you have an awareness of what an essential oil is and why. Bearing in mind the comments I have made above, some of this will be in the form of text and some in simple pyramid, table or graph form, which should, hopefully, assist you in ease of reference. My advice is to read it rather than skip it (with the excuse that you only wanted to make up a fly repellent and why bother if you do not wish to understand what it is that makes that fly repellent work). You will be surprised at the difference it makes when you can, without realising it, detect when an oil is a good one, whether it is having the effect it should or not, when you are able to pick up a bottle of, say, Jasmine, and, just from the low price and smell, know that it cannot be pure and is adulterated. All that information comes from just a little understanding of the mechanics of this subject. So, as the saying goes, 'enjoy'!

Have you ever wondered why it is that some essential oils are soothing and healing on the skin or body systems whilst other oils have irritating, sensitising and sometimes toxic effects on the skin and body? The chemical constituents of an essential oil, and how they are formed by nature, govern this. An essential oil can comprise over 200 different chemical elements. This knowledge is assimilated via a process known as *gas chromatography*. This is a test to confirm and ascertain the purity of an oil and to determine not only what chemical constituents exist within that particular oil but also if there are any traces of herbicides, biocides or pesticides which will affect the efficacy of the extracted oil. It also ascertains the levels of each chemical constituent and will therefore give an indication of how good that oil will be.

When an oil is termed 'pure', this means that it has been obtained from a botanical source without being genetically altered in any way. Gas chromatography, whilst very sophisticated, is not capable of actually pinpointing every tiny chemical constituent as many are present in only trace amounts, but with the advance of technology it has to be thought that, one day, it will be possible to analyse and note every tiny particle of an oil.

The chemistry of an essential oil basically represents three aspects:

- therapeutic properties
- odour
- hazards associated with use.

Organic chemistry itself is the study of the composition of matter. Organic matter uses a process called *photosynthesis*. This is the process through which green plants manufacture the 'food' they need to facilitate growth and reproduction. For this process to occur, the plant needs *light, water* and *carbon dioxide*. These are the three main building blocks without which growth and reproduction cannot take place.

Photosynthesis occurs when there is exposure to light. Carbon dioxide diffuses naturally from the surrounding air into the leaf via minute pores and then interacts with water, which has been absorbed by the roots of the plant in the soil, to form glucose.

It is therefore important to know how and where a plant is grown, as it absorbs everything around it. For this reason the water used around the plant should be clean and pure, as dirty, contaminated water will be taken into the plant itself and affect its quality. The soil should also be of good quality as it is from here that the plant draws its nutrients.

Few things in life are a single entity. Most are made up of a group of corresponding and complementary elements.

- An atom is the smallest part of an element that can exist.
- An element is a substance of chemically identical atoms.
- A molecule is the smallest part of an element that can exist alone.
- A compound is a structure of combined elements.
- An ion is a charged atom.

The main consistuents of an essential oil will be looked at separately as they all have a direct effect on the oil itself.

Many oils are expensive to produce and are therefore 'adulterated' by some manufacturers. This is achieved by three main methods.

- Alcohol is used to 'stretch' and 'bulk out' the extracted oil.
- Chemical constituents are removed and used to make another oil.
- Synthetic substances are added to make the oil smell better for retail purposes.

This section is a brief resumé of the groups of chemical components found in essential oils.

It is worth remembering that an essential oil is what it is because of the sum of its parts. Whilst one part might be a dermal irritant, it will always have something else to offer to the make-up of the oil as a whole. As with many things, taken in isolation certain elements may well be a risk. However, once they become part of the whole, other elements can subdue the risk element as long as that element is not present in too high a dose.

I never promised that this would be easy!

Terpenes

These are the most commonly found group of molecules to be detected in essential oils. They have certain therapeutic values in that a terpene can be *analgesic,* meaning it has pain-relieving properties. Terpenes also have a regulating effect and can be hormonal balancers.

Terpenes are divided into three groups:

- monoterpenes
- sesquiterpenes
- diterpenes.

Monoterpenes are the most naturally occurring terpenes. They have been attributed with the therapeutic function of being able to relieve pain, combat bacteria, stimulate body systems and having an expectorant effect (expulsion of sputum from the respiratory passages). Monoterpenes include limonene, found in Bergamot and Lemon.

As a note of interest, the monoterpene limonene, also found in Orange oil, is the element that makes paint dry fast. It is not always poor growing conditions that can force up the price of an oil. At one time the paint production industry bought up vast supplies of oils containing limonene, creating a shortage in the wider market. As a direct result of that action oils containing limonene (e.g. Bergamot) were very expensive that season.

Sesquiterpenes are naturally occurring but not so common. They have been attributed with milder therapeutic values and are mostly found in the 'base note' oils as they have a slower volatility rate than other compounds. They are ideal deodorising agents because of this as they inhibit the growth of odour without eliminating bacteria on healthy skin.

Sesquiterpenes include caryophyllene, found in Lavender, and chamazullene, found in Chamomile and Yarrow (this is what causes the blue colouring in Yarrow and German Chamomile, but only after the distillation process e.g. caryophyllene in Lavender).

Diterpenes are attributed with antiviral properties, can be expectorant and have a balancing effect on the endocrine system.

Oxygenated Carbons

ACIDS
Acids are not a very common component in essential oils and are found more often in the hydrolat or flower water which is a by-product of steam distillation. Acids are attributed with anti-inflammatory properties.

Acids include geranic in Geranium and salicylic acid in Birch. Salicylic acid is the building block of aspirin.

KETONES
Ketones are very toxic, especially to the nervous system, and have been known to cause epileptic fits in those susceptible to them. In the smallest amounts they can have a beneficial effect on the immune system but, generally speaking, they are such toxic compounds that they render an essential oil too hazardous to use.

Ketones include thugone, found in Sage and Thuga, and carvone, found in Spearmint.

LACTONES
These components are normally found only in expressed oils and absoluts. Coumarins, found in expressed oils, are lactone derivatives. They are attributed with being febrifuge (lowering temperature) but are also the element that causes photosensitisation.

Lactones include bergaptene in Bergamot.

ALDEHYDES
These organic molecules have high anti-inflammatory properties and act as a calming influence on the central nervous system. They are sedative and antiseptic, with some febrifugal properties.

Aldehydes include citral in Lemon and anisic aldehyde in Vanilla.

ALCOHOLS
These are divided into subgroups of monoterpenes, sesquiterpenes and diterpenes.

The **monoterpenes** have very beneficial therapeutic values in that they are antibacterial, antifungal, antiviral and good stimulants of the immune system. They are generally considered to have a 'tonic' action on the body.

Alcohols include borneol in Lavender and geraniol in Geranium.

The **sesquiterpenes** groups are rarer and differ in their therapeutic values but are still good tonics.

They include farnesol in Ylang Ylang and santalol in Sandalwood.

Diterpenes are a very much smaller group, occur only in tiny amounts, but still have therapeutic values.

They include sclareol in Clary Sage and geraniol in Geranium.

ESTERS

Esters are amongst the more gentle components of essential oils and are safer than their other counterparts. These molecules are the main ingredient that gives an oil its scent. A number of therapeutic values are attributed to this group, such as anti-inflammatory properties. As a tonic on the central nervous system, esters are also calming and sedating. They act well upon the skin and have a fungicidal action. Esters are common and can be found in most essential oils.

Esters are used extensively in the fragrance industry as they are critical to fine perfumes. The higher the ester levels the better the oil of Ylang Ylang will be.

Esters include benzyl benzoate in Benzoin.

PHENOLS

Phenols are a contradictory element of essential oils. They have strong therapeutic properties in that they are antibacterial, stimulate the immune system and have a tonic action on the nervous system. However, by equal turns they are a severe dermal irritant and prolonged use of an oil containing a high phenol content can cause damage to the mucous membranes of the body. Oils with high phenol counts should never, under any circumstances, be used undiluted.

Phenols include eugenol in Black Pepper and Nutmeg.

It has to be said here that I do use Black Pepper quite often when I need to reach the deeper muscle layers and take spasm out of them. However, I always use the oil in a highly diluted state and do take into account the type of skin and temperament of the horse to which I am applying the blend.

OXIDES

The oxide content of an oil should be noted as it can be a skin irritant in high doses. Oxides do have a limited therapeutic use in that they are a useful decongestant and mucolytic.

Oxides include cineol in Rosemary and Melissa.

COUMARINS AND FUROCOUMARINS

These are found mostly in expressed oils such as Grapefruit, Orange, Tangerine and Lemon.

Coumarins are the gentler of the two elements and are responsible for the uplifting quality of Bergamot.

Furocoumarins, on the other hand, are responsible for the photosensitive element of expressed oils, which has been discussed earlier in this chapter.

Extraction of Essential oils

The method of extraction of an essential oil from the plant differs according to the plant matter being handled. Most essential oil extraction comes under the next three headings.

STEAM DISTILLATION

This process has been used and refined over many years. In fact, it was one of the first methods used to obtain this fine substance from plant matter. It basically consists of two large vats connected by a cooling coil.

In the larger vat various parts of the plant are collected. Steam, under gentle pressure, is then forced through jets into the vat, causing the plant material to rupture and release the oil particles into the steam. The steam leaves the vat via an opening and is passed down a cooling tube into the adjacent vat. As the vapour returns to its water-bound state, the oils, which are not water-soluble, separate and lie on top of the water where they are siphoned off. The water which is a by-product of the steam distillation process (collected in the second vat) is used as a 'flower water', known also as a hydrolat. The flower water has many beneficial properties which are related to those of the oil of which it is a by-product.

SOLVENT EXTRACTION

This process involves the use of a chemical and is therefore considered by some to be inferior as they feel that residues of chemicals such as hexane and benzene must have an effect on the eventual oil obtained. Solvent extraction is a process whereby the plant material is immersed in the hexane (or other chemical) where it eventually becomes a thick paste called a 'concrete'. The concrete is then 'agitated' with pure alcohol which then releases the oil particles. The remaining material is used in the perfume industry. Some concretes remain semi-solid at room temperature and Rose is one of these.

EXPRESSION

This method is 'cold' and does not involve heat or chemicals of any kind. Quite simply, the rind of the fruit (grapefruit, orange, petitgrain, lemon, etc.) is 'expressed'. This involves placing it in a press and collecting the oil as it appears on the surface of the skin. This used to be done by hand and the oils were mopped up with a sponge as they appeared on the surface. The process now is much more refined and mechanical!

ENFLEURAGE

This method is now rarely used. Glass plates were spread with a thin layer of fat, upon which the flower petals were placed. These were left in the sun which would rupture the thin cell walls and release the oil particles. The petals would be replaced daily, the layer of fat being removed once it was saturated with oil. This is a time-consuming and expensive method of extraction.

SUPER-CRITICAL CARBON DIOXIDE EXTRACTION AND PHYTONIC PROCESS

These are the most modern methods and take half the time of the other methods. Time, as they say, is money. It has to be expected, therefore, that once the processes have been refined and the cost of operating them has lessened, which undoubtedly will happen, all oils will be obtained this way.

This is done by using carbon dioxide under very high pressure. The plant material is placed in a stainless steel tank. As carbon dioxide is injected into the tank, the pressure inside the tank builds. Under high pressure the carbon dioxide turns to liquid and acts as a solvent to extract the essential oil from the plant matter. When the pressure decreases, the carbon dioxide returns to a gaseous state which leaves no harmful residues. Opinion has it that oils extracted in this way have fresher, cleaner and crisper aromas, more similar to those of the living plants. Oils extracted in this way are more potent and the therapeutic benefits of the oils are increased.

Buying Oils

The purchase of essential oils can be an absolute minefield. They are not sold accompanied by gas chromatography readouts so that you can check the chemical constituent levels, although these can be purchased separately and, obviously, a new readout will be needed for each batch of oil. It is clear now why it is important to buy your oils from a reputable source and supplier. It is the supplier who will ensure that the oils meet all the criteria necessary before allowing the oil to be put on general sale. However, there are two elements that you should make yourself aware of when it comes to buying a good essential oil.

The first is the Latin name of the oil, which is derived from the genus and species name of the plant itself. The botanical and horticultural worlds still work with Latin names. You should take the time and effort to learn these. There are often several different varieties of an oil, all with slightly different therapeutic values in differing strengths and weaknesses. Some oils are cheaper than others of the same genus. By knowing the correct Latin name of the oil you require, you will ensure that you are purchasing the oil you want and not a different variety of it. The Latin names are not difficult and very often give a clue as to what the oil is: *Lavandula officinalis*, for example, which is Lavender; *Juniperus officinalis* which is Juniper; and names like *Piper nigrum* for Black Pepper or *Mentha piperita* for Peppermint.

It is also wise to check the country of origin as the oil will vary according to altitude, climate, soil and harvesting methods. For example, I always buy Peppermint USA as I personally find this better for *me* than the others available and I always make sure I ask for this oil by name. It is a trial and error situation, and until you have tried the different oils you cannot say what will suit you best.

Chemotype is a word that crops up often with essential oils. One way of describing a chemotype oil is basically to say that it is the same oil but different! This is due to the fact that the growing conditions may have altered in a particular area over the last few seasons, producing the same oil but with a difference in the chemical constituents and with differing therapeutic values.

Finally, when purchasing essential oils, bear in mind that you need to buy the purest and best quality oil you can afford. A pure oil is one that has not been adulterated or enhanced in any way. A quality oil refers to how therapeutically valuable it is. It is simply no use purchasing an oil that has been adulterated to a great extent and then expecting it to have the same quality as an oil that is therapeutically pure. A point to bear in mind is that the more expensive oils are very often stretched simply because if they were too expensive the general public would not buy them. Oils such as Melissa, Rose and Jasmine (the mostly 'exotic' oils) fall into this category. It is the reason why some oils are, say, £25 ($22) for 2.5ml and others only £2.50 ($3)! It is wise to remember that 5ml is 100 drops, so you are still getting 50 drops for your 2.5ml. Then bear in mind that only one to two drops may be needed at any one time so you can rationalise that, although the oil *is* expensive, 2.5ml will actually last quite a while! One example to give you is oil of Blackcurrant Bud which is very expensive. I was introduced to this wonderful oil by another aromatherapist and am now never without it. If I am feeling tired, am suffering from extreme fatigue or have been ill, a few drops of this oil will make me feel better in a very short period of time. Due to its expense, however, I do not use it for any other purpose and keep it as my own personal 'Mother's Little Helper'! The cost of it is therefore irrelevant against the therapeutic value I gain from it.

CHAPTER 7

Dilutions

A Guide to How Much Oil to Use on Different Breeds of Horses

When referred to in essential oil therapy, a dilution means the ratio of one medium when mixed with another. In this instance it is the number of drops of oil added to whatever medium you are going to use, be it carrier oil, gel, cream or lotion. It cannot be stressed strongly enough just what an important part of essential oil usage dilution is.

Because of their great strength, essential oils have to be used in the correct amounts. Overuse of an oil can cause skin irritation when the oil reacts with the mast cells in the skin, causing the release of histamine. German Chamomile is an oil with antihistamine properties and as you are no doubt aware, antihistamine creams and tablets are also available to counteract this effect. Irritation can also cause localised inflammation which affects skin and/or mucous membranes and can also result in itchiness. Irritation is also dose-dependent. This means that in the correct dilution an oil will not have this adverse effect, but as soon as too much of the oil is used, some or all of the above conditions can occur. What must also be remembered is that some reactions are idiosyncratic, meaning they will affect a particular horse even in the correct dilution. Just like us, horses are, after all, individuals.

Oils with an irritation risk are Cinnamon Leaf, Lemon and Garlic.

Sensitisation can also be caused by not adhering to the correct dilution of oil to carrier. Sensitisation is the allergic reaction to an applied oil and is shown in the form of a rash also known as urticaria. This is caused by an allergen (in this case the oil) penetrating the skin and triggering an immune response by the release of histamine. The inflammatory reaction is caused by the T-lymphocyctes being sensitised. Repeated application of the same allergen will cause the same symptoms as dermal inflammation, i.e. the skin will be blotchy and irritated in humans. In a horse this has been recorded as raised weals or lumps, with the horse showing signs of excessive rolling or rubbing to alleviate the itching.

Oils that can cause this reaction include: Ginger, Lime, Peppermint, Lemon, Tea Tree, Lemongrass (good against ticks), Bitter Orange.

These are all oils that are in regular use and it is therefore imperative that the correct dosage and dilutions are adhered to.

The problem with essential oils may be that they are used in such small amounts. A guideline might say 'add 5 drops of Peppermint to 10ml of carrier oil', for example. It is human nature, it would seem, to think we know best and to override that advice with the idea that five drops do not seem very much at all and to add more, sometimes two or three times more! This is when the problem occurs. These oils seem innocuous and five drops may seem a paltry amount when faced with a 17hh Irish hunter of dense muscle bulk, but if the direction says five drops (or whatever) then please do adhere to that advice. It has been given for a very good reason.

Dosage is also dependent on the type, temperament, size, breed and skin type of the horse. Truly a case of 'courses for horses'. It has also to be borne in mind that what suits one horse may not necessarily suit another, even if they are of the same type/breed, muscle density, size or whatever. Each application has to be treated as an individual one, germane only to that horse.

There are many different types of horses, all with different temperaments and skin types. This has to be taken into account when assessing the dilution for the horse in question. Below, guidelines are given of a fair idea of what dilution of oil to carrier should be used. Guidelines, however, are all very well, but, on the day, faced with your own horse, which you know (or should know) very well, it is for you to collate the necessary information and assess if it falls into any of the categories below. It may be that it does but that you feel, because of its temperament or whatever, you should lessen the amount of oil.

The trouble with 'guidelines' is that people often believe them to be written on tablets of stone. They read other authors who say use 20 drops instead of five. They read that certain oils could be used without diluting them first and then forget what oils those were and assume that many oils can be used this way. For every one opinion that is written you will find at least one, perhaps even two, to contradict it. There are books written by qualified people *for* qualified people. There are mountains of advice given upon the assumption that the reader will know exactly what the author is talking about. That is very often not the case at all! I have written this book from the point of view that the bulk of the readers who will pick it up know absolutely nothing, or the bare minimum, about essential oils. I have advised on usage for people who have never, or rarely, used an essential oil before. If you do not fall into this category of reader, and are much more aware or qualified with essential oils and you chose to ignore my advice that is your prerogative. For the purposes of this book, however, I will always err on the side of extreme caution.

HEAVY DUTY (DRAUGHT) HORSES
This category encompasses breeds such as Shire,
Suffolk Punch, Clydesdale, Irish Draught, etc.

These breeds are slower moving, heavyweight horses that are usually in slow, steady work. They have heavy coats as a general rule, thick skins and extremely dense muscle bulk. In size they may be anything from 15hh to maybe even 20hh. Taking as a guide measure 5ml of whatever carrier you will be using, use anything from three to five drops. Ergo, if you are making up a massage gel and you have 50ml of, say, Aloe Vera, using the per 5ml guide you may use anything from 30 to 50 drops of oil or combination of oils. You are not looking to smother the animal in a massage gel, merely to use it as a lubricant or method of getting the oils onto the horse. 50ml is actually quite an acceptable amount for this purpose.

LARGE LIGHT RIDING HORSES
This category encompasses the smaller Irish Draught,
Medium and Heavyweight Hunter types, Cleveland Bay, crossbreeds,
carriage horses and warmbloods.

Using the 5ml guide, add three to five drops of essential oil or combination of oils.

Conditions for the first category apply here also.

LARGE LIGHT HORSES (BLOOD HORSES)
This category includes Thoroughbreds and Arabs.

These horses can be of a nervy disposition and highly strung as well as sensitive. In size they can range from 14.2hh to 17hh. It is with these breeds that a good knowledge of essential oils is invaluable. There are oils with 'emotional' properties and it is these oils in particular that have to be used with the utmost care with these horses (i.e. Rose, Yarrow, Vetiver, Violet Leaf, Benzoin).

Using the 5ml guide use one to three drops per 5ml, depending on temperament and susceptibility of the horse in question.

MOUNTAIN & MOORLAND PONIES
This category includes the Dales, Fell,
Highland, Welsh Cob and Welsh Section D.

These are the heavier, but smaller, types with thicker coats and skin and dense muscle bulk, with a size ranging from 13.2hh +.

This is quite a difficult category to advise for. Whilst they have the same dense muscle bulk as the heavier horses above, they are obviously smaller and quicker both in temperament and movement. They could be deemed as falling between two stools. Therefore my advice for this category is to follow the maxim of two to four drops per 5ml of carrier, perhaps having to repeat the process a few days later. It is always best to err on the side of caution, and 'little and often' is as good advice as any to follow. It is much better than one single huge dose that the animal could not cope with.

LIGHT MOUNTAIN & MOORLAND PONIES
This category includes the Connemara, New Forest,
Exmoor (these can have a slightly stubborn nature),
Dartmoor (which can have a relatively placid nature),
Lundy and Welsh Sections A, B, C
(which can be quite nervy in temperament).

These all have slightly finer coats and skin and less muscle bulk than the Dale etc. above. Using the same 5ml guide, use between one to three drops of essential oil/s.

Massage

Head massages for all breeds should contain no more than one drop of essential oil per 5ml of carrier oil. The essential oils have a much faster and more acute effect when applied to the head and therefore the dilution should always be greater (less essential oil to carrier).

The old adage of 'less is more' is a good one to apply to the use of essential oils on horses. A human being is capable of saying that a blend is too strong and that they do not feel well because of it. The horse, however, cannot tell us this and it is therefore left to the person applying the oils to monitor and try to read the effects of the oils being applied. It is therefore equally important whilst applying essential oils that you do not lose sight of, nor ignore, your horse's body language. It is the only way they have of telling you that something is either right or wrong for them. (This is discussed further in the massage sequence chapter.)

CHAPTER 8

Successful Blending of Essential Oils

The blending of essential oils has a knack to it. It is not the same as some people's approach to cooking – put everything together in a pot, mix it, and then use it. It is not like mixing a cocktail either, where the ingredients are put in a special container and then have the living daylights shaken out of them. These oils are delicate substances that react to their environment. How they are handled has an effect upon them. The type of materials they come into contact with can affect their delicate balance. Think how carefully you would treat a fresh flower head so that it was not damaged. This is how an oil should be treated.

It is as well to remember that an essential oil needs room to breathe. It is therefore important that any blend you make does not fill the bottle or container up to the neck or lip. Leave a good 10 per cent air gap for the 'breathing' process to take place (or, in whisky-speak, a finger's width).

When blending, what you are actually doing is creating something. It is an art as much as art itself, or cooking or interior design. Therefore, how you blend these elements together has a direct effect on the resulting quality and efficacy. Blends that are cobbled together in a hurry, without much thought, rarely work to the best of their known ability. This has been proven to me many times when I have been guilty of literally throwing a blend together – sometimes even mixing it in the palm of my hand! – using it also in a hurry, and then finding that the results of that usage are less than satisfactory to say the least. The whys and wherefores of such a phenomenon, are, I believe, irrelevant. Humanity likes to rationalise everything down to the last dot over the i. It is a trait I gave up when I began working with horses, and I have now learnt that with some things it is just the way it is and that is the end of the matter. So it is with blending and using essential oils.

There are no secrets, as such, to blending essential oils with other media. There are a few ground rules to follow, perhaps, but it is more a case of common sense than something 'secret'. That said, it is, of course, no different to any other talent. There will always be those who, seemingly without effort or much thought, can bring together a number of oils and a medium and make it a superb blend. Just as there are those who can pick up a paintbrush and create a masterpiece, or use basic ingredients and yet cook up a culinary delight. There will always be those who will put oils together that no one else would think of blending and find they have a wonderful, successful, yet very different blend on their hands, whilst others doing the same will end up rejecting it as being unusable! I suppose, then, therein lies the secret, if there be such a thing, to blending essential oils.

Essential oils are so called not because they are actually oils as such, but because they are *insoluble* in water. The oils, therefore, will not be soluble in cold, water-based media. Obviously, they will dissolve on contact with hot water but once this cools the essential oil will separate and sit on top of the cooled water solution.

It is possible, however, to blend oils with water-based solutions by adding a 'surfactant'. This is a chemically produced medium which binds the two elements and allows them to remain in that state. Pure alcohol can also be used to blend oils. However, this is not easy to come by as, although some pharmacies sell it, they are dubious about selling it direct to the general public.

When making up a fly repellent, for example, 90 per cent of the blend will be water-based. A surfactant of some kind will always be needed for this.

Essential oils blend well with other oils, known as carriers, such as Sweet Almond oil, Jojoba, Avocado, Coconut, Linseed, Passion Flower, St John's Wort, Wheatgerm, etc. On the whole, however, these carrier oils are not always suitable for use on our hairy equines. Avocado, for instance, is a thick heavy oil; Passion Flower is expensive. These heavier oils can combine with the natural greasiness of a horse's coat and sit on the hair shaft. This attracts air-borne dust particles and can clog the pores. If the hair is clogged the coat will be even more greasy and unable to 'breathe' and this will defeat the object of the exercise.

Personally, I have found that by far the best medium to use on horses is Aloe Vera gel. This can be purchased in 1 litre (US 4–8floz) pots from all good essential oil suppliers and should last a fairly long time. An important point to remember here is that everything carries an energy, whether it be an essential oil, a carrier oil, a gel, a cream or a lotion. It is always important to buy the very best quality. I have purchased some Aloe gels, mainly from high street/retail outlets, and found them to be completely lacking in any energy at all, and very 'watered' down. An Aloe gel may appear an innocuous substance but it is taken from a living organism and it *will* have retained a source of energy from that plant. The cheaper the gel or medium, the more likelihood there is of it being adulterated in some way. Gels may often be 'stretched', thus reducing their level of effectiveness.

Massaging a horse is not the same as massaging a human. That may seem a rather obvious statement to make, but not to some. Human skin can be dry and flaky, making it hard to slide the hands over. Hands seem to slide naturally over a horse's coat. The use of oils in an Aloe base, applied to the horse during massage, will not affect how your hands move over the coat. You can massage as well without anything at all. Oils blended with an Aloe gel soak in immediately and do not leave a residue that can attract dirt to the coat, as carrier oils can. The rapidity of absorption of the Aloe gel means the oils will enter the bloodstream far quicker and therefore their effects will be felt sooner, rather than later.

There are other media with which essential oils blend successfully. These are shampoos, conditioners, creams, lotions and aqueous mixes. All are available, in their natural unperfumed form, from essential oil suppliers.

Where shampoos and conditioners are concerned, you can add essential oils to your normal brand, be it human or animal type, or you can buy the pure base from a supplier and add your own blend of oils. As it is quite nice to blend all of your essential oils synergistically, it would be nice to keep a litre of shampoo and make different blends for each of the horses you own, based on what suits them most at that time. These are sold at reasonable prices by oil suppliers.

As far as other media are concerned, I find creams can be too heavy, but lotions are very useful, especially for wounds and leg problems. For conditions such as mud fever I use Aloe Vera gel solutions as they are absorbed into the skin almost instantly and dry very quickly.

When using a carrier oil to blend your essential oils, do not fill your chosen container and then add the essential oils. Half fill the container, then add the oils, then add the remainder of the carrier oil. Screw the lid on firmly and then turn the bottle end over end *gently* half a dozen times. Then, holding the bottle between the palms of both hands, gently roll it backwards and forwards. This has the effect of mixing the two elements, and also warming them. As essential oils always work more efficiently when slightly warm, it is certainly worth taking the time to do this.

During the winter months it is harder to keep the oils warm. When I am going to offer oils in 5ml/10ml/20ml amounts, I find that putting the bottle next to my own skin for a few moments, allowing my warmth to infuse it, will help when it comes to using the oil because the warmth will allow the aroma to come forth. Alternatively, you can keep them in bubble wrap which has an insulating effect. Another way to stop the cold getting to blends that are kept in the stable yard is to keep them in a box surrounded by a good depth of hay.

A horse's skin (or common integument as it is sometimes referred to) is very sensitive; it can feel the smallest fly land upon it. Horses do not like cold elements applied to their skin, even in summer. The application of cold substances that have not been warmed through causes them to flinch and tense the area of application which is actually the exact opposite of what you are trying to achieve.

Some essential oil therapists are governed by the elements of top, middle or bottom notes as applied to essential oils. I am not one of these. I believe that each one of us perceives something when it comes to smell that is peculiar to the person in question. Whilst, technically speaking, these terms refer to the volatility of an oil, top note oils being those that evaporate on contact with air quicker than the middle or bottom notes, which take longer, increasingly I am finding that people refer to them more as a method of balancing a blend. There is nothing wrong with this or the advice that too many of one note may make it too sharp if all top notes have been used, and too heavy if all bottom notes have been used, but what comes into play then is the subject of perception. What I may perceive as a bottom note, someone else may believe to be a middle note and so on. Whilst, logically speaking, the most successful blends will combine a mixture of all three elements of top, middle and bottom notes, it will not make a blend 'wrong' if it contains, say, only middle notes, only top notes or only bottom notes. This is an outlook I am sure I will be castigated for by the purists! That said, it is as well to remember that bottom notes are those oils whose volatility is slower and whose aroma lingers for some time. Some of these aromas are heady – Ylang Ylang, for instance – and if these blends are too strong or do not have another element to lift them, they can linger on the receptor cells and cause headaches. Do horses suffer from headaches? I believe they do, so please bear this in mind when concocting blends.

Where you blend the oils is also important. Do not do it in an enclosed and airless space. You are likely to give yourself a headache and possibly make yourself feel nauseous. Also, the aroma will linger, which is fine up to a point if you are using something light, like Grapefruit, but a nightmare if you are using an oil such as Garlic which is pungent and actually not very pleasant. Do not mix the oils near the stabled horse as the same rules apply.

The utensils you use for blending will also have an effect on the oils you use. Do not use metals of any kind, either in containers or for mixing (bowls, spoons, etc.). They adversely affect the energy and delicate chemical balance of the oil. Plastic is not ideal but is better than metal. Do not continue to use a plastic bowl for mixing if you can still smell previous oils on its surface, even after it has been through the hot cycle of a dishwasher. It means that the oils have penetrated the surface of the bowl and this will contaminate other blends being mixed in it. Never use a plastic bowl whose sides or surfaces are already scored. Bacteria or other elements contained there will also affect your blend.

The most suitable container for mixing is a glass bowl or glass measuring jug. Glass is an element which does not retain smell. If, however, the glass surface is scored, then the same rule applies as for plastic.

When you are making up larger quantities of oils and media, say, if you are making a fly repellent, do not use metal utensils. Glass rods are available from all main essential oil suppliers and these are truly the best items to use. Hard plastic teaspoons (usually coloured) will do as a second option, but they are by no means ideal. If you are going to use these, ensure that you do not use them for anything else and that they do not become scored or 'crazed' in any way or they will retain aromas from other oils which could contaminate your blend. Some people use wooden spatulas or rods from pharmacists' beauty sections. I would not use these, but if you do choose to use them, use them only once and then throw them away.

The bottles that you use to blend your oils or keep your blends in should not have been used for other purposes if they retain an essence of what they were used for previously. If they have been used for something else but are scrupulously clean and bear no residual traces of the previous content's aroma, then it is fine to use them. They should be sterilised between uses.

Essential oils are not cheap. It is important, therefore, to understand how much to use. A small wound will need only a small amount – 5ml will actually last three days at least. To make up 30ml, which may not seem very much to the eye, is simply a waste of money and oil. It is far better to make up a small amount and to use that first, making more up if needed, than to make a large amount and waste it. Even for a 17hh horse, to whom you may wish to give a full body massage, 50ml is adequate for whatever blend you are making.

As you use the oils more frequently, you will be able to judge the amounts needed more accurately.

One last rule to remember when blending essential oils is to bear in mind the old adage that 'less is often more'. Do not use six oils when as few as two would achieve the same result. It is not cost effective, would not have three times the effect, would not work any faster, and is simply a waste of oil. I have not yet come across an equine establishment where penny-watching is not a habitual pastime.

Suggested Blends

Listed below are some blended products that you can make up yourself using the list of oils in this guidebook.

FLY REPELLENTS

These are best made up in batches of 250ml or 500ml, as you will use so much of them during a week. First there is a list of oils with fly-repellent properties, so you can decide upon your own blends, together with one or two suggested blends from me.

Suggested Oils	
Cajeput	Citronella
Eucalyptus	Eucalyptus Lemon
Eucalyptus Peppermint	Garlic
Geranium	Lavender
Lemon	Lemon Balm (not listed – use sparingly)
Lemongrass	*Litsea cubeba*
Long Leaf Pine (not listed)	Patchouli
Peppermint	Rosemary
Sandalwood	Scotch Pine
Tea Tree	Virginian Cedarwood (not listed)

Note: *Peppermint is included in the list not because it is an insecticidal oil, but because it has antipruritic properties (alleviates itching), lifts otherwise heavy or acid blends and is cooling and refreshing.*

Do not mix together any more than five oils per application – this is simply a case of overkill and a waste of oils. Even one or two oils will be fine if the energies of those two oils are compatible.

Ingredients
4 tsp Aloe Vera Barbedensis
100ml of any of the following flower waters:
Lavender/Peppermint/Chamomile/Eucalyptus
50 drops Geranium
50 drops Lavender
50 drops Sandalwood
50 drops Rosemary
50 drops Lemon

Method
Add the drops of essential oils gradually to the Aloe Vera gel and mix well with a glass rod. The gel may go white as the amount of oils added increases and they become difficult to blend. At this stage very gradually start adding the floral water. Once this is blended, make up the required amount with ionised water, adding a little at a time and blending gradually but not beating.

To this add 5 to 10ml of surfactant which will keep the oils blended. If you do not have this available, you may add 10ml of a non-perfumed shampoo which will act as a binding agent, although the surfactant is preferable. Add water to make up to 250ml.

Using the funnel, pour the mixture into a plant spray bottle. Store in a cool, dark place out of direct sunlight. Keep the nozzle free from grease and dirt.

Try a sample spray on your forearm before use and, from this, you will know whether you have made the blend too strong or too weak.

Alternative blend
50 drops Eucalyptus
50 drops Rosemary
50 drops Cajeput
30 drops Peppermint
30 drops Pine

Other ingredients as above to make up to 250ml.

SWEET ITCH LOTIONS

Sweet itch is caused by an allergic reaction to the saliva of the Culicoides fly. In this instance antihistamine effects are required, and preparations with soothing, anti-inflammatory properties. Sweet itch lotions can be used prior to the actual 'season' starting, whereby they act as a preventive, and also once itching has occurred. If the skin becomes broken because the reaction has not been caught quickly enough, see the preparation on page 116. As with the fly repellent, there are numerous oils that you can use in any combination for this situation.

Oils
- Roman Chamomile (soothing, anti-inflammatory, antihistamine action)
- German Chamomile (azulene content soothes and acts as anti-histamine agent)
- Garlic (highly repellent, use sparingly as it is a dermal irritant in high doses.) Use equal amount of Chamomile, Yarrow or Lavender to counterbalance its effects
- Yarrow (soothing, healing, anti-inflammatory, bactericidal – use in conjunction with Garlic to soften the dermal effects). (USA: if Yarrow is not available use Blue Chamomile).
- Lime (cleansing, antiseptic)
- Lavender (healing, soothing, anti-inflammatory, antiseptic)
- Niaouli (not on the list but combats insect bites)
- Seaweed (helps purify the blood if badly bitten and severe reaction has taken place)

Ingredients
50ml Aloe Vera Barbedensis gel or Aloe Vera and Seaweed gel
50ml Chamomile hydrolat
20 drops Garlic
20 drops Yarrow or Roman or German Chamomile
40 drops Lavender
30 drops Seaweed
ionised water to make up to 250ml

Method
Add the oils to the gel bit by bit until well blended. Once the gel becomes white and no longer absorbs the oil, gradually begin adding the hydrolat.

Make sure it is all well blended. Add 5-10ml of surfactant as needed. If using German Chamomile or Yarrow, you will need at least 10ml to ensure that the azulene (blue) mixes in with the rest of the ingredients. If this is not added, the azulene will gradually separate from the other ingredients and sit separately on top of the mix. If you do not use surfactant, it is important that you shake the bottle gently but firmly until the 'blue' blends in with the other ingredients.

Gradually add the water to make up to 250ml. This should now resemble a much thicker preparation than the fly repellent. If it appears too thin, add more Aloe Vera gel until it is of a quite thick but still mobile consistency. Keep it in an airtight container and out of direct sunlight. Apply either with your fingers if they are clean, or thin cotton wool pads or cut-up pieces of soft towel (half the size of a face flannel, say). Wash these through and hang to dry after each application. Applying with the fingers does ensure that you are able to massage it through the mane and tail to the skin and the dock. (If using your fingers, wipe your hands between applications, before dipping them back into the pot.) Take care not to let this trickle down the horse's face into the eye, which will cause damage. The same care should be taken around the genital area near the tail. Apply in the morning and late afternoon/early evening at which times the fly problem is at its worst. Be prepared for any solution including Garlic to be extremely pungent. It is not possible to disguise this smell due its strength. Do not keep this near the stable but in an area that is well aired and where it will not cause offence to either animal or human.

HOOF CONDITIONER
The problem with hoof 'oils' is that they can create a watertight barrier on the hoof, prevent moisture from penetrating and prevent the hoof from being able to 'breathe'. One way around this problem is to use a water-based product.

Ingredients
8 tsp Aloe Vera Barbedensis gel (40ml)
35 drops Lavender
20 drops Carrot Seed
30 drops Roman Chamomile
Chamomile hydrolat

Method

Add the oil to the gel bit by bit. Once the gel begins to turn white and will not absorb any more oil, gradually begin to add the hydrolat until the whole quantity has been used. Then add the ionised water to make up to 200ml. This solution should be mobile but quite thick in consistency. It should not be too thin and runny. Apply with a clean, unused hoof oil brush, pastry brush, or, alternatively, a large soft-bristled artist's brush. A half-inch paintbrush will also suffice. Wash these through thoroughly after each application.

Clean off the hoof with some water and a cleaning brush. Pat dry. Apply the solution as you would a hoof oil. Do not put too much on the brush or it will just run off the hoof. Paint it on.

Use each morning until the solution is finished if the hooves are bad. If they require only a maintenance application, use two to three times a week, sparingly.

SKIN ALLERGY APPLICATION
If your horse is showing the raised bumps of a systemic reaction to something and you have called the vet and he or she has given their permission for this to be applied, the following will bring relief to the horse and alleviate the symptoms. Apply two to three times daily until the allergy disappears.

Ingredients
8 tsp Aloe Vera Barbedensis gel (40ml)
70 drops Lavender
70 drops Roman Chamomile
50 drops Immortelle
150ml Chamomile hydrolat
3 tsp honey (liquid variety)

Method
Gradually add the honey and the drops to the Aloe Vera gel until it begins to turn white and will not absorb any more oil. When this happens, gradually add in the hydrolat and the remainder of the oil. Make up to 350ml with ionised water. Shake gently but firmly to ensure the honey is dispersed.

To apply you can either pour a little of the solution into the palm of your hand and smooth it over the horse's skin, or you can soak a piece of soft clean rag and run that gently over the coat. Wring it out over the horse's back and smooth in the liquid with your hand.

Wash your hands immediately after use. Avoid the horse's eyes and nostrils.

This can be applied two to three times daily until the symptoms dissipate.

EQUINE SHAMPOOS

These need only be made as you require them. A blend that is made up and kept around a yard for months, possibly with the top not back on properly, will lose both its aroma and effectiveness with the passage of time.

Oils		
Rosemary	Lime	Roman Chamomile
Ylang Ylang	Rose	Linden Blossom (not listed)
Patchouli	Tagetes	Palmarosa

Method

Base shampoos are available from all good essential oil suppliers and come in 500ml and 100ml amounts (USA 2oz to 1 gallon). It is always best to keep one of these on hand as they contain no additives and are generally of a very good quality. To each 30ml of shampoo add 20 drops of oil, either singly or in combination to suit your horse. Use in the normal way. I sometimes add 10ml of Linseed oil (carrier) to the shampoo and this seems to give the coat quite a shine.

It is not false economy to buy 500ml as the base will suit human and equine alike.

MUSCLE WASHES

There are two ways of utilising a muscle wash. One is to pour the essential oil solution into a bucket of warm water and wash the horse down with a soft cloth. The other method, which is more user-friendly when travelling, is to use the solution in a more concentrated form. These solutions should be carried in thick plastic bottles, never glass as they are easily knocked or dropped and broken glass would be a nightmare around a horse. The first method is to make up the solution

HALF PRICE BOOKS ®

Half Price Books
1835 Forms Drive
Carrollton, TX 75006
OFS OrderID   30125608

Thank you for your order, Brian Cassmassi c/o Sean Bennett!

Thank you for shopping with Half Price Books! Please contact service31@hpb.com. if you have any questions, comments or concerns about your order (687446191)

SKU	ISBN/UPC	Title & Author/Artist	Shelf ID	Qty	OrderSKU
S390033150	9780851318462	Essential Oils for Horses : A Source Book .... Carole Faith	PET2.3	1	

ORDER# 687446191
Abebooks

SHIPPED STANDARD TO:
Brian Cassmassi c/o Sean Bennett
325 N LARCHMONT BLVD # 343
LOS ANGELES CA 90004-3011
rmtbuyer@gmail.com

in a glass measuring jug and then pour it into the bucket of warm water just before use. The other method, using the concentrated solution, is to stand the bottle of solution in a bowl of boiling water to heat it through (in much the same way as a baby's bottle). Apply the wash to your own skin first to ensure that it is not too hot. About 250ml should be adequate for a single application of the concentrated solution. The solution has to be warmed through for it to have any real effect. Take a flask of hot water with you if you do not have access to living accommodation in your lorry.

The wash can either be poured directly onto the horse with your cupped hand below it to spread it immediately across the area being worked on, or you can pour it onto a flannel/cloth carried expressly for that purpose.

Oils for the relief of muscle fatigue, muscle stress and strain, aches, pains, arthritic and rheumatic conditions, etc. are listed below.

Oils
- Ginger (warming, easing)
- Juniper (disperses build up of fluids, toxins)
- Peppermint (stimulates circulation, has hot and cold properties which are beneficial to painful areas)
- Ylang Ylang (relaxant)
- Roman Chamomile (antirheumatic, anti-arthritic properties, anti-inflammatory, pain, sprains, soothing, sedative)
- Grapefruit (cleansing, disperses toxins, stimulating)
- Carrot Seed (smooth muscle relaxant)
- Vetiver (sedative, relaxing, stiff joints, sprains, aches and general pains)
- Lavender (sedative, antispasmodic, antirheumatic, general aches, pains and sprains, stimulant of circulation)
- Jasmine (sedative, general muscular aches and pains)
- Black Pepper (deeper layer muscle relaxant, anti-arthritic, anti-rheumatic, circulatory stimulant, general aches, pains and stiffening)
- Clary Sage (general aches and pains, stiff joints, sedative)
- Geranium (circulatory stimulant, bruising)
- Immortelle (bruising, anti-inflammatory, general aches, pains and strains)
- Sandalwood (stiff joints, sedative)
- Sweet Marjoram (antirheumatic, anti-arthritic, general stiffness and aches and sprains)

- Scotch Pine (circulatory stimulant, anti-arthritic, antirheumatic, general aches and pains)
- Benzoin (anti-inflammatory, sedative, circulatory stimulant, anti-arthritic
   and antirheumatic)
- Lemongrass (muscular aches and pains, circulatory stimulant, sedative)
- Rosemary (antirheumatic, fluid dispersant, circulatory stimulant)
- Lemon/Lime (anti-arthritic, antirheumatic, circulatory stimulant)

Ingredients
For bucket wash:
30 drops Peppermint
30 drops Clary Sage
20 drops Ginger
20 drops Jasmine
15ml surfactant
(The blend should have an oriental, spicy aroma to it.)

Method
Mix the oils together with the surfactant then disperse this into a bucket of water. Swish the water round until the oil can no longer be seen. Apply either with a piece of towel or another clean, soft cloth. Ensure that the water is warm enough to disperse the oils but not too hot to use.

Ingredients
For concentrated travel wash:
20 drops Sweet Marjoram
40 drops Lavender
20 drops Lemongrass
15ml surfactant
ionised water to make up to 250ml
(The blend should have a pleasantly sharp citrus scent, with a warm undertone provided by the Lavender.)

Method
Store in a thick plastic bottle that can stand in water.
Boil up a kettle and pour boiling water into a bowl deep enough to come three quarters of the way up the bottle containing the wash. Let it stand

for about 10 minutes or so. Test on your own forearm. It should be warmed through without being hot. Apply almost immediately. Do not take a bowl of hot water near the horse. Apply with a soft cloth for the best results. This method is for use on specific areas, e.g. leg, shoulder, rump, etc., rather than for all-over use.

Do not warm the mix and put it in a vacuum flask in the hope of keeping it hot. Flasks are lined with metal and this may cause a chemical reaction in the blend.

COPD *(Chronic obstructive pulmonary disorder)*

This condition seems to be increasing. I can only put this down to the increasingly domesticated circumstances under which we keep our horses, poor ventilation of this domesticity, ever more complicated foodstuff and general airborne pollutants and allergens. This condition is normally found in horses that are over two years of age. It is more common in stabled horses, for obvious reasons, i.e. dusty bedding, hay fed in nets and not soaked, poor ventilation of stables and deep littering of bedding over prolonged periods. Hot, dry weather conditions can also exacerbate the condition. In extreme cases it is sometimes necessary to put a horse on a fibrilator to assist in the breathing process, especially when the horse has begun to 'double breathe' and a 'heave line' may be showing around the belly/lower rib area. Some horses show symptoms that include a severe mucus discharge. In this instance it is prudent to turn the horse out as much as possible and keep it in as dust free an environment as possible.

COPD can also be attributed to horses that used to be known as 'broken-winded'.

You may be wondering what role essential oils have to play in such a condition. Used in association with sensible stable management practices, the condition can be dealt with very well. Bedding can be one of the worst sources of allergens and dust-extracted shavings are better than straw for a horse with this complaint. Soaked hay is always necessary to stop the spores from lodging deep in the windpipe.

The throat is an area much troubled by COPD. Just by putting your ear to the windpipe you may be able to hear a faint 'roaring' sound as the horse tries to take in enough air.

Oils that are beneficial for the throat area include **Myrrh** which is attributed with dispersing catarrh, of being balsamic, which is a soothing action, and which is warming and gentle.

Lemon Eucalyptus and **Peppermint Eucalyptus** are both good for

113

easing congestion and opening the airways, as is *Eucalyptus radiata.* All three oils make excellent chest and throat rubs.

Fennel can be used as an asthmatic. **Tea Tree** is antiseptic, balsamic, disperses catarrh and clears the airways. **Clary Sage** is a deep muscle relaxant and good for asthmatic-type complaints.

Peppermint is clearing, both for the head and sinuses. **Cajeput** is used for upper respiratory tract ailments and assisting bronchial difficulties, especially problems with the throat. **Frankincense** is soothing to the chest and throat, aiding bronchial conditions and easing asthmatic-type problems, whilst also having a sedating calming effect, thereby easing the breathing process. **Ginger** is locally warming, soothing, eases congestion and tightness, disperses catarrh and relieves dry coughing.

Sandalwood is another oil that would actively assist throat and upper respiratory tract areas, easing congestion, dispersing catarrh and having a balsamic effect on the throat. **Violet Leaf** assists bronchial disorders and is clearing and soothing. **Lavender** has many beneficial effects on the respiratory tract as a whole, including disorders of the throat. **Bergamot** will combat airborne allergens and clear the throat.

It must be noted that COPD problems will not be cured by the use of these oils and that they should not be used as an alternative to conventional medicines.

The oils will assist the congested areas, alleviating the irritant symptoms and bringing to the horse comfort from the vagaries that COPD throws up.

There is no one thing that can be done to combat this condition; it has to be a solution that is more than the sum of its parts. If taken in isolation the effects would be rendered weak; put them together, however, with everything working in synergy with every other part, and the effects are quite stunning.

With this batch of oils no more than two or three are needed.

MUD FEVER

This is the term given to a dermatological infection caused by constant wetness of the skin and being covered in mud, especially from clay-based soils. The condition can range from a few scabby areas with a bit of a discharge to the more severe cases where whole tracts of the leg are covered in sores which weep, causing crusts. The pink skin of the heels is particularly affected by this. The wetness causes the skin to crack and the bacteria in the mud get into the circulation and cause the infection. This can cause lameness and the legs to swell painfully in severe cases. In particularly wet areas it is almost impossible to avoid at least a mild case of mud fever during the winter and wet spring months. There are various preparations on the market which can help matters, a very effective one being a powder with water-repelling qualities that I would highly recommend, called Mud Guard.

There are two schools of thought as to how to deal with muddy, wet legs. One is to hose them off every day and dry them as best you can before bandaging. The other is to leave the legs alone, put wicking boots on, let them and the horse dry out naturally, and brush the dried mud off later. The problem with hosing is the cold water and a horse that is dancing about – not the easiest of tasks to complete. It is not easy to dry the legs off either, especially if the air itself is damp and everything just seems to remain in a state of constant dampness. I have tried both ways and have this year come to the conclusion that to leave the legs alone is working out by far the best option. These days wicking boots are so good that within a few hours the wetness has dried to a flaky dustiness. However, what is good for one horse is certainly not always the case for another. I have two Irish Draughts. One never gets mud fever other than a tiny patch on her white fetlock; the other suffers greatly and easily. The year 2000 was one of the wettest on record, and I would therefore assume that mud fever was a problem for many horse owners. Touch wood, in 2001 (the time of writing) neither horse has shown any signs of it.

In 2000, one of my Draughts suffered terribly. It took a few trial and error sessions with the oils to find one that dealt with everything – inflammation, soreness, bacterial infection and hair loss to name a few – but the blend given below turned out to be a magical elixir for Barney, seeing hair regrowth within seven days of application.

It is said that all applications for mud fever should be dry to combat the wetness that has caused the problem in the first place. Whilst this is true to a certain extent, it is almost impossible to implement. I used Aloe Vera gel as the base for the preparation as, although this is a 'wet' treatment, it soaks into the skin almost instantly and dries quickly without having a tightening effect. With this condition it is very important to remember that you cannot apply the preparation with your fingers and then dip them back into the pot for another dollop! You would almost certainly be transferring bacterial infection into the preparation. Most chemists sell wooden spatulas in their beauty departments, probably in boxes of 100. Use one end each time to dip into the pot and put the gel into the palm of one hand before applying it with the fingers of the other. Wash your hands immediately after application. Throw the spatulas away after use.

The first blend listed below was actually made up for cracked heels but worked so well for mud fever that I now keep a pot of it made up for all 'winter eventualities'.

Blend One
10ml Aloe Vera gel
5ml Linseed oil
10 drops Frankincense
10 drops Myrrh
10 drops Patchouli
10 drops Yarrow
Chamomile water to make up to 100ml

Add the drops gradually to the Aloe Vera gel. Blend in the Linseed oil. Gradually add the Chamomile water until the mixture is well blended and has no 'separations' in it. Store in a jar or bottle and keep out of direct light and extreme cold.

Blend Two
50ml Aloe Vera gel.
15 drops Myrrh
30 drops Frankincense.
20 drops Roman Chamomile
30 drops Lavender
10ml Green Clay
30ml Chamomile water
water to make up to 130ml

Same blending and application as for Blend One.

It seems that the 'magic' ingredient was Patchouli. I have used it on many skin problems and found it to be absolutely excellent where horses are concerned. Less so for humans for some reason.

SMALL SUPERFICIAL CUTS THAT BLEED

It is of vital importance to know when to call the vet and when to apply common sense when dealing with conditions presented to us by our horses. There is a vast difference between a muscle ripped by barbed wire fencing and a small superficial cut that is bleeding profusely. The former will need the attention of a vet at the earliest possible moment, while the latter needs common sense and something to stop the bleeding as well as being antiseptic. This blend is also suitable for use on dogs (which is when I have also used it).

By the term superficial I do mean just that – a cut or a 'nick' that is just breaking the surface of the skin – one step on from a graze.

Ingredients
20ml Aloe Vera gel
6 drops Lavender
6 drops Geranium
6 drops Myrrh

Blend the oils in gradually, as for other blends, and apply direct to the cut with a cotton bud or spatula. Spread with the fingers (which must be clean!). Do not dip your fingers into the pot once you have touched the wound.

Both Geranium and Myrrh are 'styptic' and arrest external bleeding. Do not expect this to happen the minute you apply the gel; essential oils are good but not *that* good. However, within a couple of minutes you will see a lessening of the blood flow and within five minutes it should have stopped. This blend may be applied in small amounts until this has been achieved.

GEL FOR STRAINED/PULLED MUSCLE
There are times when we are aware that our horse has overexerted itself, perhaps during a jumping session or if it has stumbled whilst out hacking and you can feel it stiffening. It may be that when running your hands over an area of muscle it feels tight and has an extreme of temperature, either hot or cold. This gel preparation helps the muscle to 'unlock', expels toxins built up from the overexertion and promotes suppleness. This can be applied as a gel, or let down enough to be used as a spray. I have used both and would not choose between them. It really is a case of personal preference.

15ml Aloe Vera gel
15 drops White Birch
15 drops Peppermint
15 drops Wintergreen
15 drops Roman Chamomile
Chamomile hydrolat (to 100ml)

Once blended this will smell like something your granny would have used back in the annals of time! It has a clinical, antiseptic smell. When you apply a tester of this to your forearm (as you should with all your blends), it will feel cold upon application but produce a feeling of heat within a very short space of time. It will feel like it is being drawn down from the surface of the skin, through the layers and down to the bone itself. It is quite powerful, so do not exceed the number of drops stated above. This is as good for humans as it is for horses and I can highly recommend it for muscles in the shoulder and arm areas for humans.

There are oils here that are not on the list of recommended oils in this book. This is because there is not enough usage for them to be on the general list, their primary use being for this type of ailment. Wintergreen and White Birch are available from all good essential oil suppliers. About 10ml of each will last you a long time.

RHEUMATISM AND ARTHRITIS MASSAGE GEL
Rheumatism is defined as being 'a painful affection of the muscles of the body, the fibrous tissues being in an inflammatory state'.

Rheumatoid arthritis is defined as being 'a wasting of the joint surfaces, the thickening of the parts around a joint and distortion due to muscular contraction'.

Arthritis is defined as being 'any inflammation of the joints'.

Horses as well as humans can be affected by these conditions. As they are degenerative there is no known cure as such. It is, however, possible to make the conditions more comfortable and ease the joints into a more workable condition. This is mainly done by the administration of drugs, either given orally or by injection. Complementary applications can help these conditions but, as with many things, the results will never be noticed overnight, rather over a prolonged period of time — sometimes it is as much as three months before the system begins to respond to what is being applied. These are considered to be acidic conditions and a balance needs to be restored to bring about a more alkaline state of being. Detoxification also helps the body to combat these painful conditions.

Diet has to be taken into account for either horses or humans suffering from these conditions. If a horse is prone to either of these, it would be as well to have their feed tested — kinesiology is very good for achieving these results — and keeping them off foods that give a weak reading and feeding only those giving a strong reading.

On the external application front, gels and lotions can help the affected areas greatly. Aloe Vera gel, even on its own, will greatly reduce the symptoms of aching joints and muscles, but it takes time. It is not a miracle cure and just as Rome was not built in a day, so one application is not going to show an effect overnight. I advocate the use of Aloe Vera gel for these conditions, with added essential oils for the condition as apparent at the time of application.

No condition stays the same, but changes, much like a kaleidoscope. In effect, what this means is that what has worked for six months will suddenly lose its effectiveness, maybe, and different oils but with similar properties must be sought and a new preparation made up. Each horse will be different, each one's system reacting differently to whatever is applied. Some will respond very quickly and results will be noticed within a short period of time; others may take months. However, once the difference has been noted, the condition continues to maintain a level, even finding a good degree of improvement in some cases.

There is no one right way to deal with these elements. Some people will prefer to use acupuncture which is proving very effective when used on horses. Others will try pressure-point work, shiatsu, and yet others will try essential oils. I make this point because essential oils are not magic potions that can work miracles. Sometimes, however, they can achieve the impossible!

When dealing with these conditions, every aspect has to be taken into account – diet, environment and workload. You cannot apply a lotion in isolation and expect it to work if the horse is living in damp, cold conditions, is left without proper protection after prolonged work, or is overworked for the conditions presenting themselves. The whole picture has to be dealt with. Deal with the external elements as well as the presenting symptoms. One will not work without the other. There are times when the joints will become inflamed and swollen. Never massage over these areas as they will be extremely painful. Apply the massage gel/lotion to the surrounding areas. It will still have the necessary effects. Once the swelling and inflammation have eased, as they will with these conditions because these symptoms are sporadic and not constant, then it is fine to massage the gel over the joint area. Even so, great care must be taken, as the joints will still be sensitive to touch.

The best way to deal with these symptoms is to take a long hard look at the overall picture. Can you improve your horse's environment, lessen draughts, keep the stable warmer, the floor warmer, the bedding thicker to give a more cushioned effect? Is the diet you are offering your horse the right one or does it need altering to suit your horse better? What about the workload? Are you ignoring the fact that your horse is perhaps getting on in years and cannot do all the things it used to? Is the weather now having more of an effect on your horse and what can you do to combat that? We do not live in the best of climates. It is very often wet and foggy. What aftercare are you giving your horse after wet, hard work? Ensure that your horse is properly rubbed down, that the circulation is increased, and that the proper measures are taken to ensure its well-being and safety – rugging up, bandaging or whatever it takes.

Overexertion can cause joint problems, most often associated with jumpers, cross country competitors and hunters. Prevention is better than cure every time. Make sure the after-activity care is the best you can offer your horse. Sometimes, if a muscle is inflamed, it is better to use a cold compress. This may seem like an awful lot of trouble to go to after a hard day's hunting or competing, when, being tired yourself, all you want to do is have a hot bath and a glass of wine. However, if you wish your horse to serve you well, and to continue with you for a long period of time, the aftercare is every bit as important as the event itself. It makes the difference between a horse that can no longer work and a horse that, despite its age, is fit, well and able.

The knack here is going to be your ability to discern between the different types of muscular aches. For example, muscular tension caused by overexertion in dry warm conditions may need different oils from tension and muscle strain in a horse that is wet, cold and tired. Inflammations may need different oils again.

There are many oils that will assist these conditions.

Peppermint (its hot and cold properties are good for overexerted muscles. It promotes circulation. It is both anti-inflammatory and antiphlogisitic, meaning it deals with muscles as well as joints) 3 drops per 5ml

Lavender (soothing, easing, relaxing, especially suited to rheumatism) 4 drops per 5ml

Sandalwood (antiphlogistic properties counteracting inflammation in joints) 4 drops per 5ml

Juniper Berry (detoxifies the body, which aids both arthritic and rheumatic conditions – especially good for rheumatism) 4 drops per 5ml

Cedarwood (antispasmodic qualities suited to arthritis and rheumatism, stimulates the circulation) 4 drops per 5ml

Roman Chamomile (excellent anti-inflammatory properties, also antiphlogistic so aids both arthritis and rheumatism) 5 drops per 5ml

German Chamomile (see Roman Chamomile above, same dose)

Black Pepper (mild pain-relieving qualities, it is antispasmodic, aids the body in expelling toxins, is stimulating to the circulation and reaches the deeper layers of muscles – a good one to use if wet and tired as it is very warming) 3 drops per 5ml

Ginger (a lovely oil to use for arthritis or rheumatism. A warming oil well suited for cold wet winter-day exertions. It has stimulating actions that work well on cold tired muscles) 3 drops per 5ml

Grapefruit, Lemon and Lime (a trinity of oils which are excellent for these conditions, as they are depurative, stimulating, cleansing (toxins, acidic conditions), antispasmodic and combat both arthritis and the effects of rheumatism) 4 drops per 5ml

Myrrh (both anti-inflammatory and antiphlogisitic which aids both arthritis and rheumatism. Myrrh is stimulating and revives tired muscles) 3 drops per 5ml

Rosemary (combats most muscular pains, has antispasmodic properties, helps dispel fluid retention, is a circulatory stimulant and can be used for both arthritis and rheumatism) 4 drops per 5ml

Sweet Marjoram (has mild pain-relieving qualities, suits both arthritic and rheumatic conditions, combats stiffness and strains) 4 drops per 5ml.

Pine, Scots (suits both arthritic and rheumatic conditions, stimulates the circulation and can be used for general muscular aches and pains) 3 drops per 5ml

Violet Leaf (mild pain-relieving qualities, anti-inflammatory and a stimulant of the circulation) 2 drops per 5ml as this oil has an effect on the emotions

Yarrow (a particularly soothing oil suited to combating arthritis and rheumatism. It is anti-inflammatory (one of the best), reduces muscle spasm, and is generally soothing) 4 drops per 5ml

Carrot Seed (helps purify the system, relaxes muscular spasms, can be used for both arthritis and rheumatism, stimulates the circulation) 3 drops per 5ml as this is quite a strong oil

Fennel (anti-inflammatory properties help to combat rheumatism, helps to purify the body systems, and is a stimulant of the circulatory system) 3 drops per 5ml

Wintergreen (not on the list but excellent for dealing with strained muscles and tendons; it has mild pain-relieving qualities, is anti-inflammatory, stimulating and can be used very effectively on rheumatism and strains) 3 drops per 5ml.

Cajeput (has antispasmodic properties which will aid rheumatism, can be used on all general aches associated with muscular problems, its antispasmodic properties also assist the chest in times of infection/tightness) 3 drops per 5ml

Vetiver (very grounding, used for muscular problems, arthritis and rheumatism, it is antispasmodic and is a circulatory stimulant) 3 drops per 5ml

From this long list of oils it is possible to make up any number of blends depending on what the circumstances are. For instance, Black Pepper and Ginger with Juniper and Grapefruit make quite an exotic and spicy blend for when your horse has been cold, wet and stiff as well as overexerted.

Peppermint, Lime and Sandalwood give a very pleasing aroma and work very well together.

Cajeput, Pine and Lemon make a good antiacidic blend, which smells as fresh as a pine forest.

Look carefully at your horse and decide, from what you know of your horse and its condition, which of the above oils would suit it best.

Do not mix together more than five oils as this is simply a case of overkill. For this type of preparation I find one to three oils works best of all.

The carrier depends on what type of massage you are undertaking. Aloe Vera gel always works well and soaks in almost immediately.

Base creams are available from essential oil suppliers. These have no additives and are perfume free. Lotions are also available.

If you are making up a wash to cover these three elements, use the hydrolats and a surfactant (this will blend the oil with the water), as all the hydrolats have traces of the properties of the oil.

Carrier oils are somewhat difficult to work with as a medium, especially if you have a hairy horse. The object of the exercise is to get this preparation onto the actual skin itself. Long hair can prevent this if the oil is just clinging to it.

Carrier oils attract dust and dirt when left on the skin and this must also be borne in mind.

ANXIETY/FRUSTRATION/NERVOUS TENSION

This is a difficult category to deal with. What constitutes anxiety, frustration and nervous tension? Is there a definitive symptom that describes all horses? The answer, I feel, is no. Each horse is very different from the next. They share similarities of symptoms perhaps, but what impulse has resulted in those symptoms manifesting may be very different indeed. Horses are unpredictable, prone to nervousness in unknown situations and can become overexcitable and hard to handle. Firstly, it is so vital to know your horse and to know it well. Observe it; what makes it tick? What frightens it, what makes it shift nervously, what makes it stare at some imagined object that has the sole purpose of coming to 'get' it? Without any of this knowledge it would be very difficult to choose an oil to help it. Some horses need grounding, some horses need teaching manners, some horses will always be afraid of their own shadow – all these feelings are different but they will share some of the same symptoms. These may manifest the day before a show when activity is more centred around your horse. It can feel that something is in the air, it will probably work out that it is a show and become excited – especially if you are nervous and pacy at the prospect of what is to come.

Horses can suffer from performance stress as much as humans – and that is mostly a human's fault. We sometimes do not realise the strength of pressure we exert upon our animals to achieve. They can feel our disappointment if something does not go well. It is not always the horse's fault either. If the rider has been giving conflicting signals, or even unclear ones, the horse will become tense and nervous. Take the whole picture into account when dealing with the presenting symptoms of your horse. Are you partly to blame? I point this out because it depends on the circumstance and symptoms as to what oil you would choose for your horse.

For example, take my horses. Barney a 17.2hh Irish Draught, who is built like a tank, has the mind of a baby. Anything and everything upsets Barney. My mood, if it is heavy and sombre, makes him anxious and he naturally wants to blame himself. If the two mares he shares his barn with are out of sight in another field his anxiety levels are sky high until he can see them again. Certain types of rain on the tin roof make him fearful for his life but thunder, lightning, and gale force winds have absolutely no effect on him whatsoever. The black wheely bin at the entrance to the driveway is only frightening on certain Tuesdays and the odd Friday. Going for a hack to a place he has never been before is tantamount to abduction and it is always a bit of a tussle to get him to agree to go down this new route. There have been occasions when he has shot backwards 100 yards in three seconds flat and almost mounted the bonnet of a car at the prospect of going down past the church instead of turning round and coming back the way he usually comes. He is unpredictable and sometimes immensely illogical.

Chance will only do things if you ask her. She is 16.2hh, an Irish Draught who has done grand things in the past – or so she would have you believe. A lorry coming up behind poses absolutely no threat whatsoever and is disdainfully ignored. A lorry coming towards you, however, which is just a dot on the horizon two miles away, is a severe threat to her life and all evasive actions must be taken until, eventually, she has worked herself up into the sort of state one would have expected of certain Victorian ladies who called for the smelling salts. Quick movements of the hands make her nervous. Loud voices with harsh edges to them make her anxious and send her to stand to the rear of the box. Indecisive actions and 'fiddling' without getting on with a job properly, most pointedly the putting on and taking off of rugs, make her snappy and disgruntled sometimes for at least an hour afterwards.

I have a Forester pony, Benji, not yet backed, who has had a rather uncertain start in life. You cannot tell Benji anything. You can discuss it with him and negotiate how you are going to proceed with a situation but anything else only results in an upset, stubborn pony, and to what end? To prove my dominance? If the end result of a discussion with him is a satisfied human and co-operative pony, where is the point of dominance?

The point I am attempting to make is that these are three equines – all prone to their own neurosis and all showing the symptoms of those neuroses via different impulses. The end results, however, are the same – an anxious or frustrated equine who needs some help in recovering its equilibrium. Take Barney. He suffers from a complex of not being good enough for the job in hand and having been told so in the past. With Barney it was his jumping. True, he may not make the top grade and go on to higher level competition. He is, however, still a very good jumper. He does not know this. He has never been told this. When faced with a jump, he becomes anxious and then bolshy when he decides, 'Well, I didn't want to do it anyway'. Back in his box he is bargy and full of himself, or so it would seem. Actually he is suffering in some small way from performance stress. It is in his eyes, etched on his face, despite what his body language is doing and saying. Know your horse. A whiff of Benzoin with Barney always 'chills him out', brings him back into balance and equilibrium. I know this because I have observed him and learnt to 'read' him. He cannot talk in the accepted sense of the word as we understand it, but he is talking loudly and clearly in horse-language!

So, learn about your horse and you will be able to choose an oil suitable for the set of circumstances presenting themselves to you – *at the time*.

Here is a list of oils that all work on an emotional level and the emotions they are best suited for. They are all best used as a single oil.

Frankincense Helps distance the heart and mind from grief and deep sadness. Good to use if a horse has lost another horse it was close to, either through sale or death (2-3 drops per 10ml).

Bergamot Lifts the spirits. This oil works spectacularly well when blended with Frankincense and is an extremely well-balanced blend (4-5 drops per 10ml).

Rosewood Good antidepressant. This is a strong oil for this emotion so use it sparingly and for a short period rather than a prolonged one (2 drops per 10ml).

Grapefruit Much renowned for use in situations where perhaps performance stress is manifesting itself. It is a cleansing, clearing oil (5 drops per 10ml).

Peppermint Eucalyptus Helps calm the nerves, gets the breathing going again if it has become shallow due to nervousness. Use sparingly as overuse can cause overstimulation (3-5 drops per 10ml).

Geranium A good oil for depression. Use sparingly as it is quite an aromatic oil. Good for horses on box rest, which are normally active and out and about (1-4 drops per 10ml depending on the temperament of the horse).

Ginger A good oil to use for nervous exhaustion. It is such a 'warm' oil too (1-4 drops per 10ml).

Ylang Ylang Very calming oil that gladdens the heart (1-5 drops per 10ml).

Violet Leaf Use this for a horse that needs 'grounding' and calming. It is strong, so use sparingly (1-3 drops per 10ml depending on the horse).

Vetiver Another grounding and calming oil. It even smells earthy and solid (1-3 drops per 10ml).

Lavender Soothing and relaxing (up to 5 drops per 10ml).

Roman Chamomile Brilliant for stomach upsets brought on by nerves and anxiety. A very good healing oil for the psyche (up to 5 drops per 10ml).

Jasmine Said to be good for bargy stallions/geldings. I have never used it or had cause to use it for this, but it does induce a feeling of deep relaxation (up to 4 drops per 10ml – this can be quite a heady oil).

To blend these oils use a 10ml bottle. Pour 5ml of the chosen carrier into the bottle, add the drops of oil, and then the remaining 5ml of the carrier oil. Screw the cap on and blend by turning the bottle gently, over and over, and then rolling it between the palms of your hands to warm it. Clasp the bottle in the fist until just the top of the neck of the bottle is showing. Do not allow the neck of the bottle to protrude from your fist as this is dangerous. The horse may lift it from your grasp and the consequences of that do not bear thinking about. Offer the oil just under the nostrils about three or four inches away. If the horse is interested it will move the required nostril over the bottle and inhale. If it is not interested this will be very apparent. The horse will sniff, turn its head away quite pointedly, or even, in some cases, turn its hind quarters to you. Respect this and do not offer the oil again.

Watch for the dilation of the nostril. It may seem as if nothing is happening, but even a slight dilation of the nostril means it is taking in the airborne particles that are evaporating from the bottle. Your horse may move one nostril over the bottle and then the other. The right-hand nostril is linked to the left-hand side of the brain, which governs your horse's functions – the way it is doing something. The left nostril is linked to the right-hand side of the brain, which governs the intuitive, creative side. Your horse may produce a Flehmen reaction at this stage, which is a curling back of the top lip towards the nostrils. This traps the aroma to be inhaled and detected in the smell receptor cells located under the blaze area. The limbic system, which governs our sense of smell and the emotions thus evoked, lies on the front of the brain.

Do not allow your horse to overinhale. A few inhalations for both nostrils is fine at any one time. Do not offer more than two or three times a day. How long you continue with this depends upon your horse and the symptoms it is presenting.

Replace the cap and put the bottle in a safe place – not your pocket where it could fall out into the bedding if you forget it is there.

CHAPTER 9

The Home Essential Oil Kit

What it Should Contain and Why

This is a potential minefield of a subject. I do know that no matter what I advise in this chapter, there will always be additions that will enhance your working kit and which I have omitted, or inclusions which some will find unnecessary. Such is the way of the world. There is nothing in this chapter that is set in stone. You can choose to disregard it completely or to follow the advice. One might say, why is a chapter needed on such a simple subject at all? The answer is that there will be those of you out there who have no idea what to get and where to get it. I know when I was starting out it came down in the end to trial and error just because I could not find simple pieces of advice anywhere.

The items that I have listed below are what I, personally, from experience, have found to be those that work best and most efficiently. Obviously you do not have to rush out and purchase every single item. As you find yourself working more and more with the oils, the pieces will just naturally accumulate.

A Suitable Container / Box / Case

This will probably be the most important piece that you find or buy. It is important that this has a lid to prevent all the items falling out and becoming dirty, especially the bottles of oils themselves. Some people use open-topped carrying trays. I find these liable to have all sorts of accidents and would advise against them. The container you choose should, ideally, be airtight, as this will combat extremes of temperature and, of course, keep the elements out. Most yards are open to the weather, a point worth bearing in mind. Many essential oil suppliers also provide wooden boxes which hold anything from six bottles to over 20. One of these may do the working essential oil therapist very well, but you still need another box to hold all the accompanying utensils. The boxes that suppliers sell will take only the small narrow bottles and not jars, tubs or larger bottles. Better, therefore, to try and locate a suitable container big enough to take everything.

I personally use a metal camera case that is hinged-shelved in layers. I keep the oils on the bottom layer, where they can remain upright, and the peripherals on the shelves. Being airtight, I can leave it in most places and it is not affected by temperature or weather conditions. It can even be left in a stable yard office or feed/tack room and the contents will still be safe. A box with a lid that is not secured is fine, but this could easily be dislodged – which is not so good if you have to travel in a car between home and stable. Most camera cases are expensive, but a good DIY outlet will sometimes have suitable alternatives. A container that keeps the bottles upright is infinitely preferable to one that means they have to lie on their side.

A Starter Selection of Essential Oils

These are the oils that I find are used most frequently, are the easiest to use, and can make up a huge combination of blends.

10ml Tea Tree (*Malaleuca alternifolia*)
10ml *Eucalyptus radiata* (note that *Eucalyptus globulus* is harsher)
10ml Lavender (*Lavandula augustifolia* or *officinalis*)
10ml Roman Chamomile (*Anthemis nobilis*)
or
10ml German Chamomile (*Chamomilia matricaria*)
10ml Rosemary (*Rosemarinus officinalis*)
10ml Peppermint (*Mentha piperita*)

I have given the choice between Roman or German Chamomile for I have found that although German Chamomile is supposed to offer the greater efficacy of the two, this does depend on the person using it. I find that Roman Chamomile works better for me every time, and yet others I know find German undisputedly the better. Try both, see how you feel with them and *trust your instinct*. There is also Moroccan Chamomile (*Chamomilia maroc*) but this has very few of the large range of therapeutic properties of the other two.

These six oils will give you a good 'working' selection which should cover most eventualities. Once you are used to handling them, you can build upon them as these oils also combine very well with a huge number of other oils.

Although 10ml may not sound much in terms of volume, do remember that it equates to 200 drops. As you will only be requiring a few at a time, 10ml is a sensible amount to purchase, especially if you are a first time buyer.

Peripherals

At least 6 10ml opaque glass bottles.
1 or 2 opaque glass jars – no need for more than 20 or 30ml size
1 or 2 hard plastic tubs, preferably opaque (30 or 50ml size, these can be purchased from most essential oil suppliers at very little cost)
6 pipettes (can be bought from chemists, herbalists or essential oil suppliers)

Use one pipette per oil – do not cross contaminate them.

Carriers

Grapeseed oil makes a very good, very cost effective carrier in the event that you do not wish to purchase other oils from suppliers, or if you have run out and need a quick carrier oil. Most supermarkets sell this. Make sure it is a light one and not one of the cheapest.

Alternatively, start out with 100ml of Sweet Almond oil as this is a good general all rounder and available from all suppliers.

Linseed oil makes a very good coat polish so perhaps 50ml would be enough as only the smallest amount is necessary.

Aloe Vera gel – my advice is to buy a litre pot from a good supplier and keep it in the fridge once it is opened. Buying gel in tubes can be expensive when most tubes are 200ml or less and would work out very much more expensive than buying the litre. Some suppliers sell Aloe Vera gel with added extract of Seaweed, which is a very good deoxidant.

To begin with I would not recommend buying creams or lotions until you have learnt to work with the more basic media.

Working Items Needed.

- Several 5ml measure plastic measuring cups of the type found on top of over-the-counter medicines and in hospitals. These are very inexpensive and are usually sold in batches of 10 or 12. They are extremely useful if you need a one-off amount, as you can mix the oils into a cup. Sterilise it thoroughly afterwards. These cups are available from most chemists and essential oil suppliers.
- It is advisable to keep one or two packs of 'handbag size' tissues in your case. These are useful for wiping around the tops of the oil bottles and to mop up spillages, amongst other things.
- A pack of self-adhesive labels. It is very important to know what is in a bottle and in what dilution. Sellotape is not a suitable item as the oils soon prevent it from sticking. The labels do not have to be huge but should at least be big enough for you to write what oils are contained in the bottle.
- Dropper inserts are a must. These have to be bought, in most instances from essential oil suppliers, but are invaluable and, of course, ensure safety. A dropper allows you to measure your blends in the precise amount of drops and limits wastage. The safety aspect of them cannot be stressed strongly enough.
- At least two or three glass stirring rods. These are available from essential oil suppliers and are a necessity. I do know that some people use wooden spatulas or rods. This is acceptable if they are discarded after use as they *will* absorb the oils you are mixing, which will affect future blends.
- A small plastic funnel for transferring blends from bowl to tub, jar or bottle. These are available from most kitchen outlets as well as oil suppliers.
- A pack of moist wipes. You must only handle oils and carriers with clean hands and it is not always possible to have access to soap and water.

- A hard-backed notebook. It is very important to record what oils you have, when they were received and when they are reaching the end of their shelf life. It is also useful for recording quickly what oils you have used for what condition and any relevant notes.
- You will need at least two pens, for obvious reasons.
- An artist's brush or pastry brush if you do not have a hoof oil brush. This is for mixes made up for the hooves. The brush must not be contaminated with hoof oil or any other preparation.
- A small pack of cotton wool buds. I advocate the use of these for applying gels and creams to wound areas. If they are double-ended use each end only once. Do not dip a used end into a pot or jar of your oil blend. This will keep the blend free from bacteria, not to mention the wound site. Fingers are not always as clean as they could be, so these small items are invaluable as part of your kit.
- When making up fly repellent it is best to make it up in larger amounts, say 250ml or even 500ml, especially if you have more than one horse. Hard plastic bottles with sturdy pump action spray nozzles can be bought at very reasonable prices from most garden centres. These are more robust than the ones sold by essential oil suppliers – an important point around a bustling yard. These can be washed and sterilised before reusing them.
- A small pair of scissors. It is quite incredible how often the need for scissors arises.
- A small bag of cotton wool pieces, pads or small roll. These are for use when cleaning around wound sites or areas you are about to apply the oils to.
- A small bottle of Hibiscrub for use in cleaning wounded areas, for washing mud from mud-fever affected areas, cuts, scrapes, bites, etc. A must-have item.
- Two or three pieces of soft towelling for use when applying compresses. An old towel cut up will do the job. Sterilise these pieces after use (the hottest cycle wash will do). Remember to replace them after use.
- And the obvious. A pack of mints for the 'client'.

You will obviously add or subtract from these items as you see fit. It is interesting to note how much more efficiently it all works if the kit is kept up together and as an entity, much as you would a first aid box.

CHAPTER 10

Massage and Hands on Horses

I see 'massage' as a generic term. It encompasses many things, and means different things to different people. I believe Pamela Hannay summed it up very succinctly when she called her book *Shiatsu Therapy for Horses*. It is a far better term, is far broader in its base meaning and bears more resemblance to what the domestic horse owner might do, than the bald term 'massage'.

What is massage? Is it a sports injury technique? Is it something chiropractors do? Is it something only those who practise shiatsu can do? What of Tellington Touch – what does that come under? Do you have to have qualifications? Do you have to spend years learning? Does it mean that the domestic horse owner has to have a professional in every time they wish to 'touch' their horses? Some would answer yes to that. I would not. Touching your horse is all about you and he/she having some sort of relationship that is not about turning up, jumping on, riding out and going home again. You should touch your horse every day. It is basic communication. It is a communication that they understand without even having to think about it.

Generally speaking, it is always best to know something about the activity you are undertaking, whether it is massage for horses or painting. Lack of knowledge can cause damage. If you know what you are doing you are less likely to cause damage to your horse.

But what constitutes a massage anyway? Two hours of pummelling and pounding? Twenty minutes' fluttering over the surface? There are so many forms of touch now that no matter what kind of touch you decide to put on your horse, you will, unwittingly and undoubtedly, be bordering on many other disciplines of touch. Lifting the flesh upwards on the leg is a form of Tellington Touch, working on the meridians is part of the shiatsu discipline – and so it goes on.

When I qualified as a masseuse on humans it was hard work and there was a set routine – which, at that time, you were expected to follow rigidly. There was no room for manoeuvre, no margin for allowing instinct to take over and follow energy flow, especially if that went against the grain of accepted thinking. It was mostly because of that rigid discipline that I disliked it so.

It was equally as hard, though, when I trained to be an aromatherapist. In that discipline, whilst there was a routine as such, you were also expected to work on a particular muscle or area and use your knowledge and instinct. If you did a movement in one way, and yet the next person was doing it another, it was accepted – which is hard to take in when you are so used to regimentation. It was a complete eye opener for me and allowed me to see for the first time that each living entity truly is an individual, with individual needs, and that the 'touch' should be tailored to those needs and the *personality* of the individual concerned.

This opened up a whole new way of approaching touching another individual. In fact, the hands-on aspect started before the client had even taken their coat off. In those first few fleeting moments of meeting someone your instinct kicks in and gives you an instant reading. Whilst this might subsequently turn out to be short of the whole picture or distorted in some part, on the whole those first instincts nearly always turned out to be the right ones. Within five minutes you have already begun to build up a mental picture of the individual in front of you, what their personality might be and how you will approach them, what body weight they are, whether any immediate areas draw your eye as being tight or unlevel. In fact, without realising it, you have already assessed how firm your touch will be, where you will start, what you will talk about or if at all, whether that person needs 20 minutes, 30 minutes or 60. It is an incredibly quick process and too much thinking can dull the edges of it.

Approaching horses is no different. You meet the rider (in my case) and you begin to form an opinion about them and their personality and, almost instantly, whether that personality is impacting on the horse in any way. Then you meet the 'client'. He is standing watching you watching him. He knows you are there for a reason and he knows the reason must be him because you are looking at him even if you are not talking about him. He is assessing you. You have already, albeit on a subliminal level, assessed him and his personality type – is he going to be nervous, is he going to be fidgety, is he frightened – all this is instantly taken into account and, without realising it, you are already formulating how you will go in and begin touching that animal.

This scenario is no different for the domestic horse owner. At least, it shouldn't be. When you decide to spend time touching your horse tell him/her that you are going to be touching them. A wary horse will not relax. If you never touch and suddenly there you are in the box running your hands all over them in every direction, they will understandably be cautious of you and perhaps try to pull away from the touch itself.

When you enter the box do not walk in, clang the door shut and just suddenly 'start'. All that will happen then is that your horse will be in one corner glaring at you and you will be in another, probably with a throbbing foot into the bargain which has just been trodden on in your horse's effort to 'get away' from this new 'thing' that is happening.

Enter the box quietly, use your voice, keep your tone soft and low and comforting. Pamela Hannay has a wonderful way of starting any communication with horses. I always used to stand at the door for a moment or two to introduce myself and this worked very well. However, Pamela enters the box and squats down until she is lower than the horse. The horse sees this as a conciliatory gesture and, when it is ready, which is rarely more than a few seconds, perhaps a minute, it will put its head down to you and almost give you permission to be there.

In that one gesture alone, the first contact has been made. I do it now even with my own horses which I have owned for years. It signals to them that there is something different from the norm in my entering the box that day. From the position of, shall we say, friendship, I talk to them, tell them why I am there. Without fail a big soft muzzle will come down to my level, nuzzle, or blow, or gently push. It is the signal 'you may begin'. It crosses bridges that you do not have to worry about later. Take no notice of those sceptics who would say 'Whatever for? What a lot of nonsense!'. View it another way. If someone walked into your home without knocking and immediately began their 'visit', would you feel comfortable? Would you not, in all honesty, say, 'Why didn't you knock?'. In fact, if it were a complete stranger you would be extremely discon-certed, your guard would go up, your senses would sharpen, your brain would begin certain mechanical operations that could end up with the production of adrenalin – and before you knew it you would be in a very uncomfortable position. Is it a friend or a foe? Do they mean me harm? These thoughts will be going through your brain before you even have time to formulate them and realise that you are thinking them. So, why should it be so different for a horse, especially a stabled one, whose only sanctuary is its box. You are invading its space by barging in and touching it.

I suspect that if I were to barge into a stranger's home and immediately start running my hands over them I would suffer a few bruises and probably feel the strong arm of the law to boot. Even if I were to barge into a home of someone I know and begin touching them, rarely would they lean in and enjoy it, but more likely lean back away from me and express extreme surprise, not only at me being there but at me touching them so suddenly. Just because it is a horse, why should you behave any differently?

Muscles

What is a muscle? The answer to that question, when posed to others, has been enlightening: 'It is hundreds of tendons – no, thousands of them – all grouped together'; 'It is something that makes you stand up'; 'It is a mass of fibrous tissue that contracts and expands to enable you to move'; 'It is something that allows you to carry heavy weights'. Quite a collection of ideas to choose from there! If you are going to give your horse hands on massage it would perhaps be wise to know exactly what a muscle is.

The definition of muscle is '*a tissue composed of elongated cells capable of contraction and relaxation to produce movement in an organ or part*'.

There are three types of muscle within the body: **smooth muscles** which are found in the body systems, such as the digestive tract; **skeletal** (sometimes known as **striated**) muscle which is responsible for the movement of the body; **cardiac muscle** which is found only in the heart.

When doing hands-on work with horses you will be touching the skeletal or striated muscle.

A skeletal muscle is composed of long, cylindrical cells known as myofibrils which, in turn, are composed of water and protein. The water content is high, giving the muscle its bulk and weight. When a muscle moves the cells move over each other in a ratchet formation, contracting the muscle. As these cells move back again, so the muscle relaxes and stretches out again.

Problems occur when the cylindrical cells, working in their ratchet fashion, do not do so smoothly or do not stretch out again smoothly, leaving some cells uneven and unable to release, which is where tightness, inflammation and stiffness occur.

There is obviously very much more to the muscular system than the brief outline here. What we are concerned with in this chapter, however, is the definition of just what a muscle, as a single entity, actually is.

A muscle needs energy to be able to work to the best of its capacity. This is achieved through a substance called glycogen, which is released from within the muscle cells to enable movement. Oxygen is also required and this is carried in the blood. Waste material from this process is carbon dioxide.

This is a very simplistic version of what a muscle is, and what it does. Whole chapters could be written about it but what we are primarily concerned with here, is just having some idea of what it is you are touching.

Muscles need to be bound to other muscles and also to the skeleton. This is achieved via tendons and ligaments. These three elements cannot be detached from each other. Take away one of the elements and there is a problem. The three elements need to work in harmony with each other or a serious problem will arise.

Tendons and Ligaments

What is a tendon? It is continuous fibrous connective tissue, which attaches muscle to bone or to other muscles. Tendons have a poor blood supply, therefore nutrients being brought to them via the circulation are limited, hence the long healing time needed for damaged tendons. Tendons cannot renew themselves once damaged, and whilst scar tissue will form to repair damage, this will always leave a weakness around the damaged area. In the normal course of events, it takes up to six months for collagen to renew itself within the tendons of the lower leg. This protein is vital to the health and well-being of the tendon.

Tendons affected by injury cannot be expected to be in full working order again within a matter of days or weeks. Tendon injuries must always be considered as requiring a long-term recovery.

Ligaments are yellow and white fibrous tissue. They have some degree of elasticity through the yellow tissue but not through the white. Their function is to hold bones together, to direct the movement of tendons and to support or suspend. Ligaments are concerned with the movements of joints. They have poor blood supply but a wealth of sensory nerves. Again, due to poor blood supply they are very slow to heal should injury occur. Ligaments can maintain a degree of stretching, but as they are inelastic in some cases, injuries can be caused by overworking or overstretching.

Sprains in the joints occur when the ligaments are stretched and the limit they enforce on the joints is superseded.

Massage and Hands On

These are the three primary elements being worked upon when hands-on massage is being done to your horse.

This brings us back to the original question: 'What is massage?'. I prefer to call it hands on as this, I feel, covers a broader base. Hands on is more about touching your horse, gentle manipulation of muscle bulk, communication and a means of checking where your horse's weak spots are, where there are points of extreme heat and coldness, where there appear to be areas of tightness, and a form of relaxation or stimulation for your horse.

The question most often asked is 'Where do I start?'. If you had ten people and asked them that question, you would probably get at least six different answers.

There are no hard and fast rules about where to start or what you do – but you must decide what you are going to do before you start. Be positive about it and, above all, be realistic. Do not go out with the intention of giving a 'full works' routine only to find half-way through that you have run out of time and must leave to do other things. Time is always at a premium with most people I know. Therefore it is important to work on the areas chosen quietly, steadily and within the time frame you have set yourself.

For example, some days just do the stretching exercises. On other days decide to work on the head alone. There will be days when you want to work on the legs if your horse has been working hard. Another time it might feel as if your horse is stiff in the neck and could do with a gentle once over. You may feel that you want to work on the bladder meridian and stretches. All of these are acceptable ways of putting your hands on horses. It is far better to spend 20 minutes doing something thoroughly and well, than to spend an hour rushing through every single movement you can remember or cram in.

The following picture sequence takes this into account. It is not a 'routine' for you to follow but a series of movements for you to look at, emulate and build into a session that suits both you and your horse and the time-scale you may have to spare. Some horses simply do not like their ears being touched, for example, so work on the face and, gradually, over a few sessions, begin to work up to the ears, even just stroking them gently until your horse realises it is a pleasure rather than something to be afraid of.

Above all, the one movement that should never be left out is the flat hand exploration – the preliminary movement to everything else you do. Approach your horse quietly and gently. Place your hand on the neck, stand for a second or two, then gradually move your hands over the entire body, including the legs, and let your hands do the reading. Let your instinct take over and not your 'thinking' mind. Close your eyes if it helps. Envisage what it is your hands are feeling. It should only take five minutes to do this. It is, however, the most valuable five minutes of the time you will spend on your horse. If your horse flinches, note the area, see what it is that is causing your horse to flinch or ripple the muscle. Is it hot; is it cold? Is there a bite that is irritating the skin? Is there the beginning of mud fever? Has your horse cut himself and you hadn't noticed – all this can be shown up in just the five minutes it takes to do the exploration. At the end of whatever movements you choose to do, repeat the exercise – run the hands over the entire body, not so fast that you miss what your hands are reading, but not so slow as to almost be doing a massage routine. Trust your instincts. You will be surprised what they tell you. Listen to your horse; watch his body language. Learn the difference between the ears going back as a signal to you to stop because the horse does not like what you are doing, and it being a state of utter relaxation. My mare's ears literally go flat to her head and point backwards when she is in this state. Her face, however, is soft, the eyes closed, the mouth easy. Read the signs – this is as an important an aspect of hands on horses as the actual movements themselves.

There is one important point that I would like to stress regarding this subject. Is there a right or a wrong time to do a hands-on session with your horse? The answer is – absolutely. One has to approach the subject logically. Would you like to be fiddled about with straight after a meal when all you want to do is either prostrate yourself on the nearest sofa and read the papers or take time out for a catnap and let your meal digest? The answer is, more than likely, no, you would not. The same applies to your horse. After a meal, most horses have a 'quiet time', when they either stand and snooze or are happy just munching at their hay net, and this should be respected. Conversely, immediately prior to a meal is definitely not a time to be going about your session. The moment that first clatter of nuts into a bowl can be heard, even if it is at a hundred paces, you are lost. Horses have a body clock just as we do. They *know* when it is a mealtime and it is absolutely pointless trying to get them to settle whilst you practise a body section on them.

A vigorous session before bedtime is probably not a good idea either. If you are too enthusiastic in your hands on and get the horse worked up, he will take ages to relax again and will be very restless at being in when he would rather be out kicking his heels up.

Late morning and mid afternoon are good times as this is far enough away from mealtimes for horses to be able to relax and not be in an expectant mood.

Other points to consider may seem obvious, but are sometimes too obvious to be apparent. For example, do not do your session with an audience. The horse will not relax; he will feel vulnerable at being stared at and you will not receive or give the best that is possible for the session.

Do not talk to someone all the way through so that your concentration is directed away from the task in hand. Horses are notoriously fickle about attention. The moment they suspect that it has wandered, even by a single degree, is when they will choose to pull one of their favourite tricks, which is usually when someone gets a bruised foot or is pushed up against the stable wall or whatever other tricks are in your horse's repertoire – and they will be there, rest assured.

Do not try to do your session around a time when the yard is busy and bustling. Your horse is a naturally curious animal and will want to see what is happening, who is coming and going, who is perhaps going off in a lorry somewhere, and will pick up on the excitement of a 'competition day' or 'hunting day'. If horses are being turned out and are clattering past the box as you are attempting your session, your horse will not relax but will try to see what they might be missing out on and nothing will be gained from your attempts at trying a relaxing hands-on session!

Do not try to attempt a session if a farrier is working close at hand. You will never get your horse to stand still and relax. Move to another box temporarily if you can so that you have some distance between yourself and whatever the disturbance may be.

Do not try to start the session if you are flustered. It will be a complete waste of time, the horse will pick up on your mood and fidget and you will become even more irritable. If you have been held up in traffic, if you are stressed slightly from a day at work, when nothing at all has gone your way and you need to get into the stables and out again, but now you are late and therefore must rush everything – don't! Take time out to sit quietly for a few minutes and then assess what time you have left and decide what you are going to do with that time. Work on just the legs, perhaps, and a series of stretches. Just do a head massage. Maybe just work the bladder meridian and the tail. Do not try to cram in a whole series of movements because you think you have to, because you think that is how it should be done. It is meant to be a pleasure for both of you, not a chore. There is no point rushing in, tearing through a routine, and feeling even more worn out and frazzled at the end of it when you simply don't *have* to. This might seem a rather obvious point to make, but when you are not thinking straight even the most glaringly obvious points can be overlooked. A five-minute session worked at a steady, quiet pace will achieve far more than 20 minutes of rushing movements that have achieved everything in the sequence but actually given no benefit at all.

Music is a favourite around most yards. There always seems to be a radio somewhere, blasting out pop music. Pop music is fine but remember that a horse's hearing is twice as sensitive as yours. Whilst you might not mind pop music blasting out at a high decibel level, your horse might. It certainly will not help to promote a relaxing situation. Turn the music down, or change to something relaxing – it works for equines just as for humans. Your horse may even learn to associate the music with the hands-on session, realise that it is about to happen and therefore just naturally feel relaxed.

The whole point of the exercise is about promoting a state of relaxation in your horse. It is a point worth bearing in mind before you start.

One final point. Enjoy it. Inhale the oils, enjoy the movements, for, if you do, your horse will too. If you are relaxed and comfortable, your horse will be relaxed and comfortable. Do not go into the box bad tempered or with the idea of using the session to rid yourself of your frustration over another matter. Be calm and be part of the experience. It is, you will find, quite an uplifting one.

Hands On

FLAT HAND EXPLORATION/EFFLEURAGE
Photo 10.1

Flat hand work is very important when used in touching horses and, indeed, all massage work. When used to link other massage movements, and to end other touching sequences, it is also known as effleurage. Using the flat of your hand, in varying pressures, allows you to feel for areas of tightness, heat, cold, muscle flinch and general muscle tone. If you did no more than a flat hand exploration of your horse every day, from head to rear, you would soon have a better understanding of how your horse works, where its weak spots occur, where there is often muscle tension, which side is being worked harder than the other perhaps, or just know that your horse is in balance.

Flat hand work could and should be done as part of the grooming routine. This is also a comforting movement, and one which most horses respond to. The movement should be smooth and sweeping, not jerky and disjointed.

When using it to link other massage sequences it is also used to assist the flow of circulation which may have been blocked, and this movement helps push the blood flow through, past the area of blockage. This movement is essential after stimulating work such as tapotement (see below) as it soothes and settles the nerve endings. *Various pressures can be used for different protuberances, throat and face, or over heavier or dense muscle.*

When touching horses it is important to remember to create a 'circuit' by placing the non-working hand at a comfortable distance from the working hand. A free non-working hand allows an outflow of energy and creates the wrong balance. Another important point to remember is that all horses are different and will react accordingly – where one likes being touched another horse may not. Be prepared at all times.

CUPPED HAND WORK/TAPOTEMENT
Photo 10.2

This movement is used to stimulate rather than to soothe like the previous movement. Common sense is required when using this. For example, you would not use this on the head, throat, legs or over sensitive organs. It is used to increase the circulation and movement in dense muscle bulk. Do not use it over the spine – think how you would feel if someone hit you up and down your spine. It would be uncomfortable.

The hand should be cupped in a pyramid shape, the pads at the end of the fingers flat on the skin. The heel of your palm should also be in contact. Raise and lower the hand 3-4 inches from the muscle. You should hear an echo/hollow sound as you make contact. The movement should be fairly quick without being sharp – too slow and you will not be using this movement to its full benefit.

Use this movement about a dozen times before stopping and then use the effleurage movement over the same area, to soothe the nerve endings and aid the flow of circulation.

Use tapotement over the shoulders and the dense muscle area of the rump. With the hands facing in the same direction all the time, angle your wrists and turn your body as necessary to cover the area being worked on. This movement can be done using both hands at the same time. If using only one hand, do not forget to create the 'circuit' by placing your other, non-working, hand on the horse. Do not forget to re-create the circuit when using the effleurage movement in between groups of tapotement work. Never start your hands-on routine with this movement and be aware of your horse's reactions at all times.

Photo 10.3

Photo 10.4

There are other ways of executing a tapotement movement as well as the cupped hand shown in photo 10.2. This movement, which aims to increase the circulation, can be done using your fist, whereby you drum the end of the fist onto the muscle bulk as in photo 10.3, or by clasping both hands together, fingers entwined and using the flat back of the hand to stimulate the muscle bulk and circulation, as in photo 10.4.

FINGERTIP WORK/FRICTIONS

Fingertip work is not as easy as it looks. What is easy is getting the pressure of the fingertips wrong. The movement is not designed to dig into the skin, although there should be firm, even pressure. Push too hard and it will hurt; too soft a movement will achieve nothing. Fingertip work is used for 'friction' or stimulating the local circulation and works well on muscles that have gone into spasm, as it encourages circulation and movement.

The fingertips are also used when working along the bladder meridian especially. Meridians criss cross the body like a motorway network and are our energy channels. They can be felt in some instances as slight grooves under the skin.

Stimulation work does not have to be fast and furious. As much can be achieved by gentle but firm, consistent work as by going in 'all guns blazing'.

Photo 10.5 shows fingertip work being used around the edges of the shoulder muscle which can sometimes become tight. Photo 10.6 shows fingertip work along the bladder meridian which runs the whole length of the body and can become blocked. Ten minutes two or three times a week, just working through this meridian, is very beneficial to your horse. Note that the non-working hand is creating the full circuit. There are times when energy just needs enough stimulus to encourage its movement. Loose-wristed fingertip frictions act upon this very well. Keep the wrist supple and, with the fingers very slightly apart, use a to and fro motion very quickly over the area where you feel the blockage/tightness/spasm. Use effleurage movements after the frictions to soothe the nerve endings.

Fingertips are also used to execute the circular movements that are found in the Tellington Touch sequences. Using the tip of the middle finger with light pressure, perform one and a half circles on the spot, pushing the skin slightly as you go, and pressing slightly more firmly downwards at the end of the half circle. This finishes the movement. Immediately move on to the next area. Keep the non-working hand within a comfortable distance of the working hand. Maintain contact. Your fingertips are sensitive areas, so listen to them for, without doubt, as you are touching your horse they will be giving you all sorts of information. They will tell you, for instance, which way your horse's energy is flowing. For this reason some people may wish to work left to right or anti-clockwise on the circles as opposed to clockwise. Feel, listen, and act.

If there is too much external stimulus for you, close your eyes and let your fingers feel and tell you what to do. It is also a case of trusting your instinct. Try not to overthink the procedure. Clear your mind and just feel the task in hand – and act upon what you feel. You may feel self-conscious at first and wonder if you are imagining that area of tightness – but once you can truly 'let go' and just let the information at the tips of your fingers filter through to your subconscious, you will find the horse relaxes and responds.

Some Dos and Don'ts for Hands-on Work

The first four pictures in this chapter show you the position the hand should be in for each movement. The next set of pictures show the position you should be in, body-wise, for executing the movements required. Your own stance when executing a massage routine is as important as the movement you are making. If your own position is wrong, the movement you are attempting will also be wrong, added to which you will soon tire and begin to ache yourself.

Photo 10.5

Photo 10.6

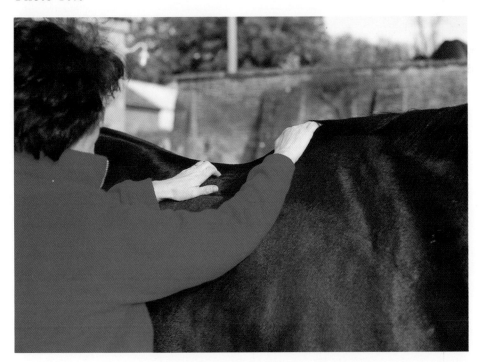

Photo 10.7   Photo 10.8

In photo 10.7, Melissa's position is wrong. Her lower back is under strain, as are her knees. She will not be putting the correct emphasis through her hands in the first position either. Within a few minutes her neck and back will be tired and the muscles on the back of the thigh and then the front of the thigh will begin to tire and ache.

In photo 10.8, Melissa is facing the direction in which she is working, thereby correcting her balance and enabling her to use her weight to push the emphasis of the movement through her hand. One leg is slightly behind, and soft, the other forward with the weight falling easily into the 'soft' forward knee. The trailing leg should be working from the ball of the foot, pushing the energy through into the other leg in a rhythmic backwards and forwards motion. The non-working hand is in a comfortable position and the working arm is using the balanced weight distribution to do the 'work', thus preventing it from tiring, especially in the upper arm area.

Room to Work Safely

Horses are unpredictable creatures. The old adage of 'always expect the unexpected' should be held as true around horses. Some are solid and grounded and a bomb going off would not make them flinch. Others are spooked by the merest movement – a hose dragging along the ground for example, the clang of a bucket, that scary broom going by that has been waiting its chance to pounce and has picked this precise moment to do so. In these instances, when horses decide to move, they nearly always do so suddenly and without warning. Your own safety must be paramount when working around horses. Therefore, when you are working on a horse, especially in a stable, make sure you have enough room to move and, more important, to move out of the way, should anything occur to make your horse jump. The bodyweight of a horse is obviously far far greater than our own, and being crushed up against a stable wall is a scenario best avoided.

In photo 10.9, Melissa is working far too close to the stable wall. There is simply not enough room for her to move out of the way if something should spook Chance (the horse she is working on) or if Melissa happens to find a sensitive spot – which is not unknown.

In photograph 10.10 Melissa has left a much greater margin for error and has

Photo 10.9

Photo 10.10

more than enough room to move out of the way should Chance decide to dance about her stable – also not unknown!

Think 'safety' whatever it is you are doing and however well you think you know your horse.

Working safely at the rear end of a horse could be the difference between a broken rib or not as the case may be. Wherever you are working on a horse, whether it be in a stable or outside in the yard, ensure that there is enough room for you to move comfortably and to move out of the way quickly should the need arise to do so.

Photo 10.11, has been stage managed for the benefit of this chapter. I would never, in the normal course of events, allow myself to get into this position – it is simply asking for trouble.

Photo 10.11

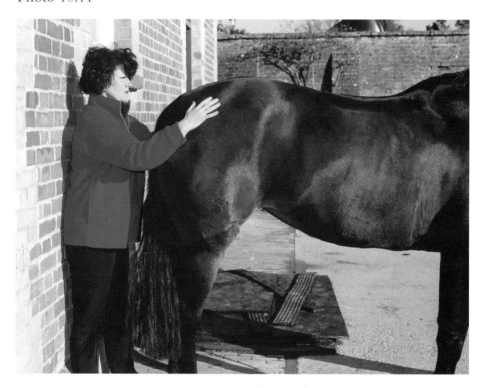

Melissa, working in the stable environment, is also in an untenable position in photo 10.12 – and it is definitely not one to be smiling at! Chance, the horse being used for demonstration purposes here, is a 16:2hh Irish Draught Hackney cross, with plenty of bone and muscle. Melissa would certainly know all about it if Chance jumped back or kicked out for any reason.

Photo 10.12

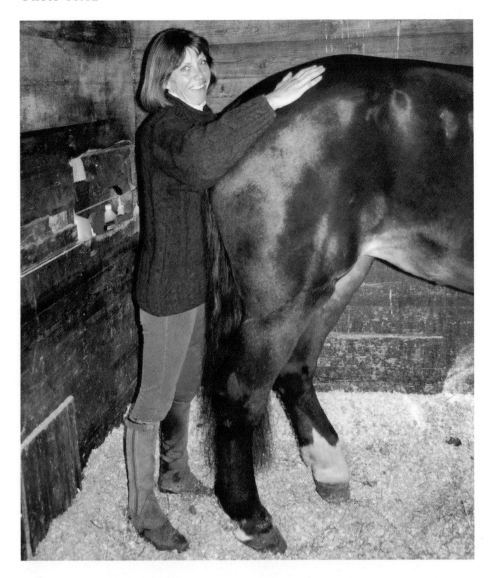

When working on the rear end of a horse, stand to the side and leave yourself plenty of room. Only trained therapists such as chiropractors and vets should ever need to be in the position whereby they are directly behind a horse. It is not enough to say that you know your horse very well and you will be fine – try telling that to the insurance company when you are off work due to an injury sustained in this way.

Expect the unexpected to happen; be aware and be safe. Never allow yourself to be in either of the positions shown in photos 10.11 or 10.12.

151

SOME ADVICE WHEN WORKING ON THE TAIL

The tail is an area that should not be forgotten when working on horses. All that hair holds a lot of static energy, and the dock itself can hold a lot of tension. Do horses have a sense of modesty? In truth, we shall never know. However, what cannot be disputed is their sense of vulnerability, and this should be remembered when working on the tail. When working on this area, I have found that by far the best results have been achieved when the arm holding the dock for support is in the 'underarm' position (as in photograph 10.13), as opposed to the 'over arm' position in photograph 10.14.

*Remember that you are using the arm merely as a prop to hold the tail **slightly** away from the body as you work on that area. If the horse feels uncomfortable and 'exposed', which can happen with the position in photograph 10.14, it will not relax and you will not be able to execute the movements required in this area with ease. Watch your horse's body language – it will soon tell you whether it is comfortable with the working position or not.*

Photo 10.13

Photo 10.14

As I mentioned in the early part of this chapter, I am not an advocate of 'the whole body massage'. Practicality dictates that the achievement of a full massage routine is going to be impossible most of the time. I am a horse owner myself and know precisely, down to the last five minutes, how much time I have to spend on any one application before moving on to the next, what will have to wait until later and what can be left until tomorrow. Every horse owner I know has to balance and juggle their time with the commitments they have. It is, therefore, unrealistic to send you out into the stable and say 'go forth and do a full body massage'. Nine out of ten of you simply would not have the time. The answer, therefore, is to break the whole thing down into modules, whereby, depending on the time you have available, you will be able to do at least something, and do it well and not in a hurried manner. The other aspect of doing it this way is that you will be more *inclined* to do something if the whole routine is broken down into smaller modules.

I am sure there would be a great deal of enthusiasm for a first time all over massage. However, the next time you may have to go into work early, or the vet is due, or the farrier, and suddenly time is once again at a premium. You may only have 20 minutes to spare – if in that 20 minutes you can work on an area of your horse as a complete unit of work, then I feel that is far better than not bothering at all because you *only* had 20 minutes and a full body treatment would obviously take far too long. There are those who will decry this attitude and say nothing can be as effective as that of 'the whole'. Not so. A 10-minute head massage can be invaluable to a nervous horse waiting in a lorry at a competition whilst its travelling companion has disappeared from view to compete. Equally, 10-15 minutes spent on a leg sequence, whilst waiting under the same circumstances, is a useful application of time, benefits the horse and gives it something to think about.

Those 15 minutes you have to spare before the farrier arrives can most profitably be spent in a flat-hand exploration of your horse, checking out areas of tension and hot and cold spots, and will also relax your horse.

Most horse owners I know own horses because they like to ride. Whilst at weekends there may be more time than during the week for this activity, if you want a two-hour or longer session then time is still going to be tight. My advice is to set aside a morning, once a month, and then, instead of riding, spend the time solely on the horse – full body massage, mane and tail trimming, washing, whatever. You will both gain the maximum benefit from this attitude. Remember, a full body work-out is not actually compulsory. It must not be forgotten, either, that in this frenetic world you yourself may be absolutely dog-tired and really not energetic enough to spend an hour and a half on physical exertion. Fifteen minutes may well do far more good in the long run.

HEAD MASSAGE SEQUENCE.

This is an ideal lone sequence, which can also be part of a whole body session. The head massage, if done correctly, can be of great benefit to your horse and is a nice way of spending a quiet 15 minutes with him or her, the added benefit of which will be an improvement in your relationship. The head massage is deeply relaxing, helps horses overcome head-shy problems, and can be used as a 'quiet time' activity between you and your horse, especially if the horse is on box rest. All your movements should be especially soft, gentle but firm. Horses do not like feathery movements, particularly around the head. This massage works well when used in

Photo 10.15

Photo 10.16

conjunction with essential oils. Make up a solution of 10ml of Aloe Vera gel and 1 drop only of a favoured oil – Lavender, Jasmine or Ylang Ylang are good choices. Smooth this along the leading edges of the ear and leave for one or two minutes before commencing the sequence. This allows time for you to clean your hands thoroughly to avoid getting oil in the eyes or nostrils, and for the aroma to be picked up by the nasal sensors and begin working.

Begin the sequence by working over the eye with a soft cupped hand in a stroking motion. Note the difference between photos 10.15 and 10.16. In photo 10.15 the horse's eye is relaxed, the ears are forward, and there is no tension in the face at all. In photo 10.16 the fingers are digging in where they should be resting on the surface. Chance's ears are showing signs of resistance and her head is up, with both her face and neck showing signs of tension. Melissa is having to reach too high to be able to work on the area in comfort.

In photo 10.15 Bess's head is down and relaxed, making it easier for me to work on her. This movement is very comforting and I use it both first thing in the morning when greeting the horses in their boxes at feed time, and last thing at night before 'lights out'.

Cup the hand and sweep it over the top of the eye socket, not so slowly that you are hardly moving but gently, rhythmically and in a flowing motion. Your non-working hand should be cupped at a comfortable place on the jaw line as both a support and to create the circuit. Do this to each eye about six times.

The next movement should be a gentle pinch along the top of the eye socket along the line of bone, working from the inside corner to the outside edge. Keep the movement soft and flowing and repeat four times on each side.

FINGERTIP WORK
This has to be done with the right amount of pressure to ensure that you are not 'digging in'.

Using the very tips of your fingers lightly but firmly work along under the eye socket, working from the inside corner to the outer point. The movement should be a light pulsating one as you move along the line. After each pulsation movement, smooth over the area worked on with an effleurage (stroking) movement. Do four sets of these on each side. The non-working hand should be maintaining a light contact on the lower jaw, supporting the horse's head and bringing balance to your own stance.

Using the thumb and forefinger and starting at the base of the outside edge of the ear, make small pulsing squeezes up the edge to the point, squeeze gently, hold,

Photo 10.17

Photo 10.18

and then work down the other edge. Repeat two or three times on each side. The ears are very sensitive so work quietly and carefully. Many horses do not like being touched here, but quiet perseverance over a few days may accustom them to the movement. The non-working hand should still be maintaining a light contact on the lower jaw.

Photo 10.19

Working on the nostrils is sometimes a new and peculiar sensation for a horse. Do not hurry this movement and do not squeeze too hard. Ideally, the non-working hand should be flat on the opposite cheek to the nostril you are working on. In photo 19, Melissa has had to hold the lead rope to keep Chance's attention focused on her and not on the lesson that had just begun over in the sand school! However, note the expression on Chance's face and her eyes which are relaxed and virtually closed. There is no tension in her face whatsoever. Start at the top edge of the nostril and gently but firmly squeeze down to the bottom right corner of the nostril. Repeat on each side about three to four times.

All of these movements can be done in isolation and can be used in various situations when a calming influence is required. The nostril movement is particularly calming and I often use it on its own as a comforter or just when we are having a quiet moment together. If you are in any doubt at all about how any of these movements feel, practise them on someone at home or in the yard. They are the same movements I use for human head and face massage. The other person will be able to tell you if you are pressing too hard or too softly, and if you have never worked on the head area of a horse before, another human is as good a practice guinea pig as any!

When working on the forelock area, which is part of the head routine, there are a few basic rules to observe. Photo 10.20 shows the wrong way to do this sequence, and photo 10.21 shows the correct way.

In photo 10.20, note the position of the non-working hand. It is holding the head collar and exerting a pressure that Bess clearly finds uncomfortable. If she decided to pull back suddenly away from that pressure, the muzzle would crack me straight on the chin, especially as I am standing too close. This could cause me to bite my tongue or even put my teeth through my lip. In holding the head collar with the non-working hand, I am also pulling the head into my upper chest area – if Bess suddenly lunged forward, with me still holding the head collar, I could well find myself falling backwards and even getting trodden on. The other drawback of the non-working hand holding the head collar is that it is not creating the 'circuit' needed for these movements to work more efficiently.

Also, note the horse's expression in the first photograph as opposed to the second one. Bess looks distinctly uncomfortable and tense in the first, almost giving the impression that she is ready to pull backwards at the drop of a hat. In the second, she is totally relaxed, the eyes are softer, the ears at a comfortable angle and she is deriving maximum benefit from what is being done. The non-working hand is

Photo 10.20

Photo 10.21

creating the 'circuit' and also acts as a support for the head as it drops slightly when (as most horses will do) Bess drops her head as she relaxes.

Note that in photo 10.21, I am standing a pace or two back, my working arm is more relaxed and not having to stretch too far, and Bess's muzzle is positioned slightly sideways on to my chest area, so that, in the event of her moving forward suddenly, she would naturally move slightly past my torso and give me the opportunity to side-step should I need to do so.

The object of this exercise is to release the tension in the forelock area. Slide your fingers through the forelock until the hair is caught at the top of the palm. Gather the fingers together and move the forelock clockwise as a whole. Do this movement three times, then repeat in an anticlockwise direction.

Smooth the forelock area down with an effleurage (stroking) movement after you have completed this.

Sliding the fingers back again until you have reached where the hair emerges from the skin, gently but firmly begin sliding the fingers back through the hair in a slight pulsing motion until the hair slips from your fingers as you reach the end of the forelock. Smooth over with an effleurage movement and repeat three times.

STRETCHING SEQUENCE

This stretching sequence may seem to be in a peculiar place in the scheme of things. This is due to the fact that I believe a series of stretches can be used at any time, whether at the beginning of body work, at the end of it, or even for a horse on box rest who cannot do much else. At least with a series of stretch movements, you are achieving some degree of suppleness. I believe that it is even ideal as a precursor to a ridden session. How many athletes do we see limbering up and stretching out before they run or train? They certainly would not think about skipping that session of vital movement. Yet, all too often we are quite content to brush a horse down, put on the tack and take off out of the yard. It may be a cold day, your horse may not be as young as it was, the weather may have been bad and it has had to spend a good deal of time in the stable – and we still just expect it to set off and trot, canter, or whatever we ask of it. A horse is not a machine. It needs the same due care and attention that we would give ourselves before a strenuous work out. These stretching exercises can be used any time and anywhere.

One of the main points to remember with this sequence is that the stretches should be completed on both sides. The idea of the stretches is for your horse to do just that – stretch – and not move its entire body just to reach the reward you may be offering.

Photo 10.22 shows a neck stretch that will be felt down the whole spine if executed correctly. Your horse may try to step back a pace to take the carrot. Try not to allow this for a horse should be quite able to reach the carrot in this position.

Photos 10.23 and 10.24 are designed to encourage the horse to stretch round sideways.

Stand level with the rib cage and hold the carrot so that it can be seen but not so that your arm is extended. The tactic the horse sometimes employs here is to walk the hind legs round so that your horse is level with the carrot. Only reward the horse with the carrot if he/she has bodily remained stationary and has stretched his/her neck round for it.

Photos 10.25 and 10.26 are asking a lot of a horse that is stiff or perhaps has not performed this stretch for a long time, or ever at all in some cases. It may take time for the muscles to elongate and stretch — so do not hurry this one. Once again, the horse may try to walk round to take the reward. Discourage this. Repeat these stretches on the opposite side. One set per side is ample.

On the first few days this may take as long as 15 minutes. However, once the horse becomes more supple and also becomes used to the routine, it will come down to a matter of minutes.

Photo 10.22

Photo 10.23

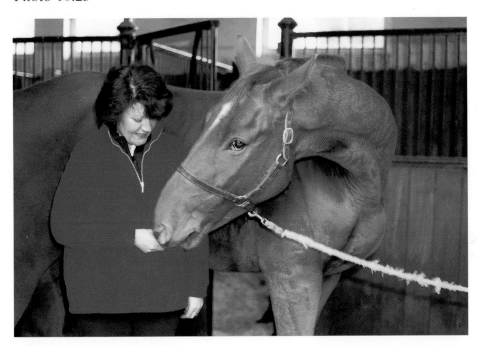

Photo 10.24

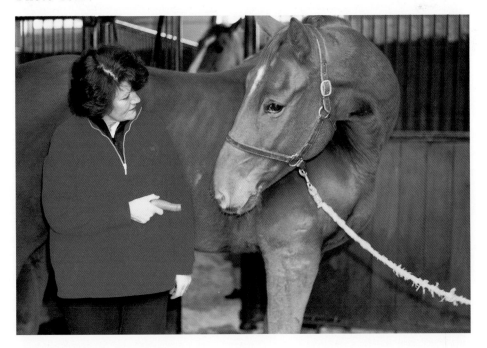

Photo 10.25

Photo 10.26

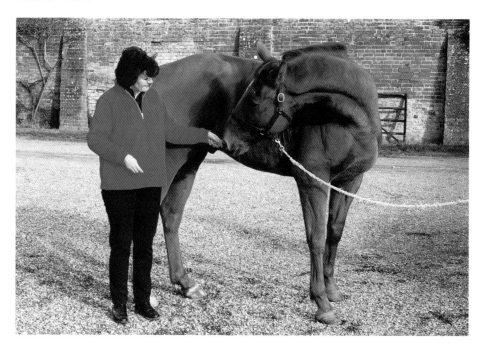

THE BODY SEQUENCE

The body section can be executed in many different ways, and there are many books describing differing ways of approaching this section. The point to remember here is that you are using the massage as a means of facilitating the carriage of the oils round the body by increasing the circulation flow. Ergo, it is not a sports massage, or one in which you have to thump the living daylights out of muscle mass. The massage should be firm, but gentle, rhythmic and flowing and be a means of relaxing the horse and taking the strain out of this area. It is also quite a tiring area to work on due to the muscle bulk – so pace yourself. Make sure that you are in the best position possible to execute the movements, not so much sparingly, but without overdoing it so that by the end of the sequence you are tired and therefore the massage is not benefiting the horse as much as it might do.

If you are working on a pony or a 15hh horse, you may be able to stand on the ground and still attain the correct angle for working along the spinal and dorsal areas. However, if you have a 16hh plus to work on, you may find it easier to stand on a box so that your arms are at the right angle to work comfortably and will not tire easily. A bucket (as shown in photo 10.27) will not do as it does not have a

Photo 10.27

broad enough base to ensure that you are working safely. An upturned milk crate or other such sturdy article is by far the best. Even a bale of straw or hay will do. The box that you use does not have to be higher than a milk crate as being too high will also put you at the wrong angle for attaining the best results from the massage.

This next sequence of photographs deals with the area from the poll to the beginning of the tail, but does not include the legs which are dealt with later.

Photo 10.28

Start on the neck. One of the techniques I like to employ here is one of the Tellington Touch movements. These are small circles executed with the pad of the middle finger. The circles – which are actually one and a half circles to be precise – should be soft without being ticklish. Do one full circle, followed by half a circle, at the end of which you should press the middle finger downwards as if you were doing a full stop. You should be almost pushing the skin ahead of the pad of the finger. The pressure you are applying for the circles should be, say, 5, based on the scale of 1 being barely touching and 10 being a heavy touch. The pressure at the end of the

second semi-circle should be in the region of 7. These circular movements may not seem to be doing or achieving very much, but they are having quite an effect under the skin. They are stimulating and yet relaxing. Try them on a friend or even on yourself. You will know if you are doing them correctly simply by how they feel on your own or your friend's skin.

The energy pattern of each horse and that of the person giving the touch is different. On some horses you may want to make the circles, and indeed any other movements, clockwise, on others, it will simply feel right to move in an anticlockwise motion. You should trust this instinct and simply follow the energy flow – feel your way rather than see your way. Once you have worked a series of circles from the top of the neck down to the bottom, use the effleurage movement in a firm sweeping motion, before going back to the top of the neck and covering another area. Always maintain contact with the non-working hand. This movement can be used virtually anywhere on the body.

Muscles being worked on in this area: brachiocephalic, splenius, trapezius, ventral serratus.

The next movement on the neck, shown in photo 10.29, is light, open-fingered friction work, working from the top down to the bottom in 2 to 3in

Photo 10.29

wide strips. Always use the effleurage movement over the area you have just covered before moving on to work on the next strip down the neck. Open finger work is also a stimulating move. Slide the pads of the fingers and then allow the rest of the fingers to make contact, including the padded area at the top of the palm. This movement works well on the main body rather than the legs and head where it is inappropriate.

Muscles being worked on in this area: as photo 10.28.

Photo 10.30

Photo 10.30 shows fingertip work around the shoulder area where a lot of tension can be held.

Your touch can be deeper here than on the neck due to the muscle bulk. Tapotement work of a gentle pummelling nature can also be used in this area. The thumbs are good tools for these muscles which can tighten and need deeper work to release them. Use both thumbs in a butterfly motion, pressing then circulating, pressing then circulating. Use the effleurage movement after each set of tapotement or friction movements.

Muscles being worked on in this area: deltoid, triceps and around the brachialis.

Working along the mane (photo 10.31) is important as, once again, this is an area that takes a lot of strain and holds a great deal of tension. Slide your fingers through the very bottom of the mane and clasp them over the spine. Moving the hands gently in opposite directions, pull one hand towards you and push the other one away from you. Work from the poll to the withers then soothe with effleurage movements at least three times. Go back to the poll area and this time run your fingers through the bottom of the mane and then clasp your fingers around the skin and lift and release, lift and release. Work your way down to the withers and go over the area with effleurage movements.

Photo 10.31

Pushing the mane over to one side and using your thumbs in the butterfly motion noted above, work from the poll to the withers in fairly fast, fairly deep circular movements, smoothing over each time with effleurage movements.

Muscles being worked on in this area: rhomboid muscle, cervical edge of splenius muscle, cervical edge of trapezius muscle, thoracic edge of trapezius.

Photo 10.32

This area is where the horse takes the weight of the rider and saddle and it therefore needs attention regularly. Muscles can be become very tight along this dorsal part of the back and the bladder meridian which runs through here can often be blocked. This area lends itself to fingertip work. Work from the withers to the end of the rib cage as one section. About an inch down from the spine you will feel a groove – this is the bladder meridian. This meridian splits and another groove runs about two inches below it. With gentle exploration you will be able to find this groove. Once you have done this, begin pulsating fingertip work along it. You may see the muscles shudder, which shows that you are moving an area of tension. Use effleurage movements in between the fingertip work. Go over this area about three times. Flat hand work should be used over the rib cage and abdomen. No friction or tapotement work should ever be done here. This is

especially important to note when dealing with the abdomen area for under this area lie the bladder, kidneys, and liver – all sensitive organs very near the surface.

Muscles being worked on in this area: the lumbodorsal fascia, the lattisimus dorsii, external intercostals muscles, external abdominal oblique.

Photo 10.33–35

This last section is for the hind quarters. Work from the croup to the dip in the leg about a foot above the hock. All movements can be carried out here. Use the effleurage movement to start you off, progress to the thumbs working in a butterfly motion all over this area, smooth with effleurage, then do two sessions of tapotement (with fists in a pummelling motion, cupped hands or the back of the hands when clasped together). Use effleurage between each tapotement session. Finally, work on the groove of the semi-tendinosis muscle which runs from just above the tail over the curve of the rump and down into the dip mentioned above. This muscle can often be tight and pulsing fingertip work through it, coupled with effleurage, is very effective.

In the photos Chance is still wearing her rug, folded in half depending on the area being worked on. Massage can release toxins in the body which can have the *effect of making the subject either horse or human, feel cold. Cover the horse up completely when the sequence is finished. Even in summer you should use a sheet after the sequence, if only for an hour.*

Muscles being worked on in this area: superficial gluteal muscle, biceps femoris, semitendinosis, gluteal fascia, tensor muscle, lateral femoral fascia.

THE LEGS

There is an old horseman's adage that says 'no foot — no horse'. This is true. However, my personal feelings are that this should be extended to include the legs. The muscles often get attention, the bones are often looked at and dealt with by a chiropractor — but what of the legs? These need a good deal of care, thought and looking after. It is not enough to rub them down with a wad of straw or hay and think you have done your bit. The legs sometimes need the circulation moving, they need stretching and sometimes just soothing. I make up a leg gel now and again, with cool 'spring' type oils in it (Grapefruit, Lemon, Lime, Bergamot, but also Lavender, Sandalwood and Chamomile), that helps to disperse toxin build up, improve the circulation and is just part of a nice 15-20 minute session that benefits the horse. If your horse is arthritic or rheumatic, it is especially important to give attention to the legs.

Some horses are nervous of being touched around the legs so start this section off as usual with the effleurage movements down the legs. Let the horse get used to the fact that you are around his feet, that you will be crouched down, and that there is nothing to fear from this.

The first movement I like to do is a friction one, albeit a gentle one. Working from the top of the leg down and then back up again, place your hands on either side of the leg, with yourself positioned just to the side of the leg. Now rub your hands together gently but rhythmically. Soothe down with effleurage movements in between the two sessions of frictions. This is a good general warm up for the leg. I also like to finish with this movement. See Photo 10.45 in the photo sequence.

The next movement is the thumbs in a butterfly motion as noted above. Work your way up the groove of the lower leg, up and over the knee, and up along the radius to the top of the leg. Smooth upwards with effleurage movements in between the three sessions of thumb work.

Next, using your thumbs, pulsate around the edge of the hoof, working from the centre out and round towards the rear. Use your thumbs to smooth this out. Repeat twice.

Leg stretching is not everyone's cup of tea and some people will be unable to do these stretches if they have a bad back themselves or problems with their hips — as, indeed, I do. However, they are fairly easy and I am even instructing my ten-year-old daughter how to do them. Your own posture is vitally important here, so if you have any weakness at all, my suggestion is you leave the leg stretches to those more physically able than yourself.

First, pick the leg up as if you are going to pick the hoof out. Gradually work your hands up until one hand is supporting the knee and the other is letting the hoof rest in the upturned hand. Now begin to rotate the hoof down to the ground so that the hoof edge alone is resting there.

Lift the leg again and work your hands up until you can clasp your hands behind the elbow. Walk back a pace. Gradually work your hands down towards the knee and step back a pace again, bending your own body as you step backwards. Now, in one fluid movement, step back again with one leg crouched beneath you and the other stretched out in front of you, balancing both you and the weight of the horse's leg you are holding. Hold, stretch until you feel the muscle in the horse's leg reach its point of resistance and then, using the same fluid movement, take the leg back to its normal position. Repeat once on all four legs.

These photos show Tracy doing leg lift stretches. Your own stance has to be correct for this so that you do not put strain on your back or stomach muscles.

Photo 10.36

Photo 10.37

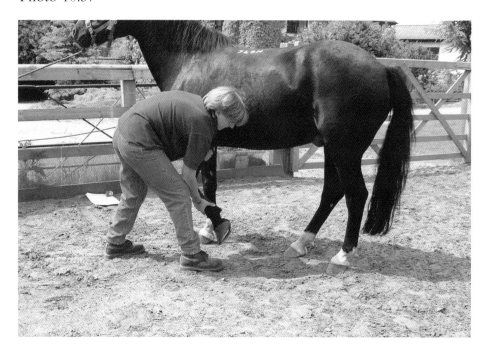

Photo 10.38

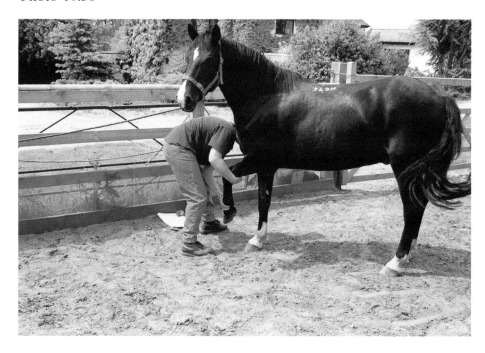

Photo 10.39

Photo 10.40

In photo 10.40 Tracy has lifted the leg from behind the knee with her own hands firmly clasped. Lay the leg along your thigh and gently stretch it forward, using your own leg as a weight bearer. The movement should be slow and rhythmical. Three small slow stretches are sufficient. Replace leg.

Photo 10.41

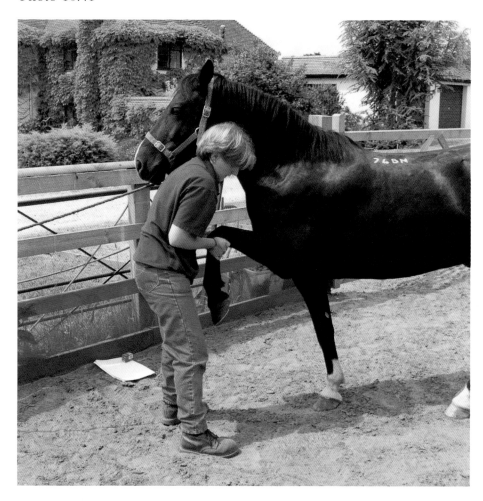

In photo 10.41 the leg lift is much higher. Make sure you are standing with both feet firmly planted, and about two feet apart. There is strain on the lower back with this movement, especially if you try to bring the leg up too quickly from a standing start position. Bring the leg up gradually and softly. It should be level with your solar plexus, hold for a count of three and release slowly back down to the ground.

The rear stretches follow exactly the same principle, and the same attention must be given to your own posture. Many of these stretching movements can be found in the discipline of shiatsu, and I would highly recommend that you read Pamela Hannay's book, Shiatsu Therapy for Horses, *for more information on stretching the legs.*

Photo 10.42

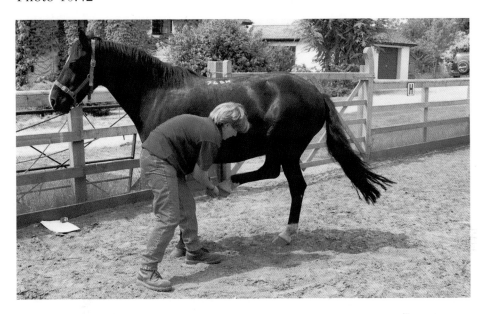

Photo 10.43

Photos 10.42 and 10.43 show a forward stretch of the hind leg. Using your nearside hand, grasp the leg behind the fetlock, then gradually lift and bring the leg forward. Support yourself by placing your other hand on your offside knee. Hold this position for the count of three.

In photo 10.43 Tracy has extended the forward leg stretch of the hind leg. Begin as for 10.42 and then move your hands around to the hoof, lifting the leg and extending it at the same time. Hold for a count of three, before releasing the leg slowly back to the ground.

Do not overextend the leg as this will cause the horse to feel unbalanced and, more than likely, it will snatch the leg away from you.

Photo 10.44

Photo 10.44 shows the hind leg being stretched out and back – a stretch you will often see a horse perform itself. Pick the hoof up and cup it in the offside hand with your nearside hand supporting the leg midway between the fetlock and the hock. Your own stance is important once again, as this stretch puts strain on the lower

back if you are not balanced properly. Your nearside leg is your 'plant' and the leg that will give you stability. Your offside leg is your 'moving leg' and will allow you to execute the movement smoothly and without strain. Your offside leg should be forward of your nearside leg, cupping the hoof, and supporting the horse's leg. Use your offside leg to step backwards and to crouch down in one fluid movement, stretching the leg with you as you go. Stretch until you feel the point of resistance and then release and move forward again, also in one fluid movement.

Remember, when working on the other leg, to reverse your own leg movements.

Photo 10.45

I have put the photo of this movement in here as opposed to where it is first mentioned at the beginning of this section, because this is the movement I like to finish with. Whatever stretches I have done, I like to just finish with thumb work on the leg, followed by soothing effleurage movements.

Leg stretches are important and can be done as an isolated set of exercises. However, they should be done carefully and with a good deal of thought. Do not hurry them and then just let the leg drop back to the ground. Tracy, who very kindly demonstrated the leg stretches for this sequence, is a qualified equine sports physiotherapist, and even she finds some of these exercises a strain. I would highly recommend at least one session with a qualified therapist, so that you can learn the correct positions both for yourself and your horse.

TAIL WORK
Photo 10.46

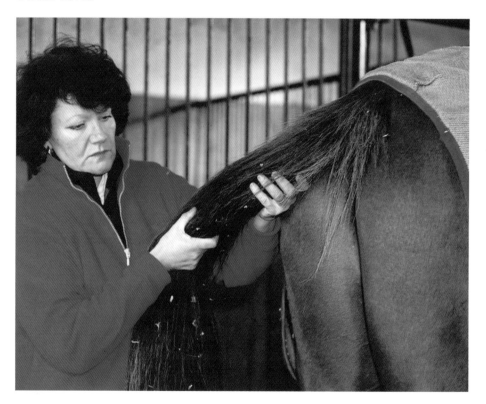

The tail should not be forgotten when working on horses. It is, after all, an extension of the spine and can hold a lot of tension. It has to be remembered that horses can easily be made to feel vulnerable. When working on the tail I have found that by far the best results have been achieved when the arm supporting the dock is in the underarm position, as in photo 10.13. Remember that you are using the arm merely as a prop to hold the tail slightly away from the body as you work on it. If

the horse feels uncomfortable and 'exposed', which can happen with the overarm position, the horse will not relax and you will not be able to execute the movements required in this area with ease. Watch your horse's body language – it will soon tell you whether it is comfortable with the position you have the tail in.

Begin the tail work by taking the dock, as shown in photo 10.46, one hand above the other. Take it to the side and stretch. Hold for a count of three and release. Repeat on both sides.

Rotations help to release tension and energy blocks. Hold the tail as above and simply rotate it, first one way, and then the other. Do six rotations on each side.

Photo 10.47

The movement shown in photo 10.47 emulates one of those used in the human Indian head massage. It relieves static and tension and gives a feeling of release.

Starting at the top, pull your fingers through the hair as shown in photo 10.47.

Gently but firmly pull your fingers through the section with small 'pulsing' movements or 'tugs'. These should be gentle and not make the horse flinch.

Repeat twice.

Photo 10.48

When you reach the end of the tail, flick your fingers as if shaking off the static energy. When finished, run your entire cupped hands down the tail and shake your hands before repeating. On the day these photographs were taken, the weather was freezing cold. A fact that is evident in my face! The horse I was working on took a while to relax due to the cold air rushing in as its tail was lifted, so please bear this in mind and do not become irritated if the horse is reluctant to have its tail moved under such circumstances.

Photo 10.49

This last movement can be used at the beginning, just at the end, or as a start and finish to the tail routine. Support the dock with one hand and clasp the entire width of the tail in the other. Begin to slide the hand slowly down the tail, moving the hand from under the dock as you do so. As you slide the hand holding the tail down, clasp the other hand above it and begin to lean your body weight back into your coccyx. Stretch the entire tail using your bodyweight. Hold for a count of three and release. Repeat once more.

This stretches the whole of the spine along the back and down through the tail. Some horses are nervous of activity happening around their rear end. Do not do this movement on a horse that is known to kick out, for obvious reasons. Do not pull so hard that you cause the horse to step backwards. Gentle, firm but slow movements are the requirements.

CHAPTER 11

Recording the Use of Essential Oils

It is very important to record what essential oils you have used, on whom and, equally important, why. It is not unknown for a horse to have an individual reaction to an oil. In the event that a vet needs to be called or, indeed, you need to speak with a qualified therapist, you will be able to inform him or her exactly what has been administered, in what amount and what dilution.

Keep a record card – even if you have only one horse. It will serve as a historical reference point and you will be able, at a glance, to see what you used for what condition and assess whether it is suitable to use again. Sometimes you will make up a blend that is absolutely wonderful and which would merit being used again. We might like to think we can remember what we used four months ago, say, but the likelihood is that we will not. Even if we remember the oils, we may not remember how much of each one went to make up that blend. It has to be said, of course, that it is just as easy not to bother, but I know from experience that there will always come a time when you wish you had.

Essential oils are not innocuous substances – they have to be treated with care and respect. Recording your use of them shows a responsible attitude and will greatly assist a vet's attitude towards *you*, should you ever need to call one out to your horse for reasons connected to your use of the oils.

You do not have to buy special forms; you can type them to your own specification, even handwrite them, but they should contain some, if not all, of the following information.

- Name of the horse the oils are being applied to.
- Colour of horse – it may not always be you reading the record.
- Any distinctive markings – same comment as above.
- Age of the horse.
- Any medications being taken by the horse at the time of the application of oils.
- Reasons why.
- What injuries your horse may have suffered in the last two years – there may be a connection to the present condition.
- What operations/veterinary attention your horse has had in the last two years – again there may be a connection to the present condition.
- Any areas of contra-indications (these are reasons why an application or area should be avoided, i.e. injury, open wound, etc.).
- A brief outline of your horse's diet – there may be a connection to the presenting problem.
- Any known allergies.
- The stress/fatigue levels of your horse (i.e. whether they are poor, fair or good; this may have a bearing on the presenting problem).
- The usual energy levels of your horse (same comments as above).
- Your horse's weight (you may not know exactly but can record if it has risen or dropped off as this, too, may have a bearing on the presenting problem).
- The skin type/coat type of your horse (i.e. fine, coarse, smooth, rough, greasy – by noting this simple fact you may realise that there has been a change.
- Muscle tone (learn to assess this for the same reasons given above).
- Your horse's digestive system (i.e. good doer, poor doer, likes and dislikes, etc.).
- Areas considered to be most under stress (i.e. withers, shoulder, back, legs, etc.).
- Injury sites if any, how they occurred, when and what, if any, treatment was given (i.e. vet, chiropractor, massage, compress, etc.).

By the time you reach this part of your record you will already have learnt something about your horse that you did not know, have forgotten or overlooked. It may make a difference to what you would at first have chosen to use on your horse. This is also part of the purpose of the record form – getting to know your horse. Knowing your horse inside out is the whole key to the successful use of essential oils and to your relationship with that horse. Cars have a service regularly – why not horses?

The last part of the form should contain the following information:

* Carrier oil/gel used and why.
* Essential oils used and why.
* Dilution (how much carrier, how many drops of oil).
* Effects of treatment (fill this in the next day or when a change is visible).

This record should be kept in a safe place and added to as needed.

CHAPTER 12

Demystifying and Understanding Essential Oil Terminology

Every subject has a terminology connected with it. Essential oil therapy is no different. Sometimes a terminology will speak for itself. Mostly, however, it needs explaining to those wholly unfamiliar with such strange words. Listed below are the main terms that you will find used in conjunction with essential oils. This list is not, by any means, exhaustive. An understanding of these terms will help you when researching certain oils and will enable you to understand exactly what it is these oils will do and how to apply them to whatever condition is presenting itself at the time.

Analgesic relieves pain. Some oils are only mildly analgesic, others act more strongly (e.g. Lavender).

Anti-anaemic promotes red blood cells and combats the fatigue associated with this anaemia (e.g. Roman Chamomile).

Antibiotic oils are capable of helping to destroy micro-organisms, especially bacteria (e.g. Tea Tree).

Antidepressant helps alleviate depression by lifting the spirits (e.g. Bergamot).

Antihaemorrhagic refers to oils which assist in the arrest of bleeding (e.g. Geranium, Myrrh).

Anti-inflammatory refers to oils that reduce inflammation which is the body's response to injury and is a protection mechanism. Prolonged inflammation, however, can inhibit the healing process (e.g. Roman Chamomile).

Antimicrobial refers to oils which combat micro-organisms within the body (e.g. Lavender).

Antirheumatic refers to oils which help alleviate the acidic condition affecting joints, muscles or connective tissue (e.g. Sandalwood).

Antiseptic refers to oils which help clear an area of contamination (e.g. Tea Tree, Lemon).

Antispasmodic refers to oils that prevent or arrest spasms (e.g. Lavender).

Antiviral refers to oils which will boost the immune System and combat viral invasion of the body Systems in general (e.g. Bergamot)

Aperitif refers to oils which encourage the appetite (e.g. Ginger).

Astringent refers to oils which assist the contraction of body tissues (e.g. Lemon).

Bactericidal refers to oils which help combat bacteria in the body (i.e. Tea Tree).

Carminative refers to oils which help reduce build up of wind in the stomach (e.g. Peppermint).

Cephalic refers to oils which stimulate brain activity, clearing the head, aiding concentration (e.g. Rosemary).

Cytophylactic refers to oils that assist the body's cell renewal process (e.g. Rosemary).

Decongestant refers to oils that assist in the clearing of the sinuses and nasal cavities (e.g. Peppermint, Eucalyptus).

Depurative refers to oils that assist the body in the purification processes (e.g. Grapefruit).

Detoxifying refers to oils that help cleanse toxins from the body (e.g. Juniper).

Diuretic refers to oils that help increase urinal flow (e.g. Sandalwood).

Expectorant refers to oils that assist in chest conditions, helping to disperse build up of sputum (e.g. Myrrh, Frankincense).

Febrifuge refers to oils that assist in reducing feverish conditions (e.g. Rosemary to promote sweating, Peppermint for its cooling properties).

Fungicidal refers to oils that will combat conditions such as thrush (e.g. Tea Tree, Patchouli).

Hepatic refers to oils that have a beneficial effect upon the liver (e.g. Carrot Seed, Lime).

Homeostatic and Styptic refer to oils that assist the arrest of external bleeding (e.g. Myrrh, Geranium).

Hormonal refers to oils that help to regulate hormonal secretions (e.g. Geranium).

Hypertensive refers to oils that assist the body to raise blood pressure (e.g. Lavender).

Hypotensive refers to oils that help lower and regulate blood pressure (e.g. Lemon – can be used for either condition).

Immuno-stimulant refers to oils that assist the body's natural defences (e.g. Rosemary).

Insecticidal refers to oils that repel flies, insects, etc. (e.g. Eucalyptus).

Laxative refers to oils that increase bowel movements (e.g. Black Pepper).

Nervine refers to oils that assist the well-being of the central nervous system (e.g. Lavender, Chamomile).

Parasiticidal refers to oils that help combat parasites (e.g. Lavender).

Relaxant refers to oils that have a relaxing, sedative quality (e.g. Vetiver).

Rubefacient refers to oils that increase the circulation and are locally warming (e.g. Rosemary, Black Pepper).

Sedative refers to oils that have a deeply calming effect (e.g. Violet Leaf).

Stimulant refers to oils that have an invigorating effect (e.g. Peppermint).

Stomachic refers to oils that are beneficial to the stomach (e.g. Sweet Orange/Sweet Fennel).

Styptic (see Homeostatic).

Tonic refers to oils that have a beneficial effect on the body systems in general (e.g. Ginger, Vetiver).

Vasoconstrictor refers to oils that help the blood vessels to contract (e.g. Lemon, Peppermint).

Vasodilatory refers to oils that assist in the expansion of blood vessels (e.g. Sweet Marjoram).

Vulnerary refers to oils that assist in the healing processes (e.g. German/Roman Chamomile).

There are many other terms attributed to conditions of the body and relating to the therapeutic values of essential oils. This list will cover most eventualities, however, and whilst you may come across other terms in your dealings with essential oils, you will find that most of them can be cross-referenced with the broad base of terms listed here.

CHAPTER 13

Equine Publications and Aromatherapy Books and Journals

The equine world is changing. That is an indisputable fact. Whilst many of the old ways will endure, change is inevitable and also much needed if any progress is to be made. There is now a huge swing towards a more holistic way of treating animals in general. It has to be said, however, that you should never plunge in without testing the water first. If you wish to avail yourself of holistic care for your horse, you should read as much on the subject as you can. Information is power. It is as well to know whether the information being provided to you is of any worth or not.

Where publications are concerned I am not aware of too many that deal with the subject of essential oils *and* horses. The answer here, then, is to treat this as two subjects and read all you can on both. If you know as much as you possibly can about essential oils and what they do, then you will also understand what they can do for your horse and whether or not they would be suitable for the use you have planned. It does not necessarily follow that an essential oil will be found for every ailment, cut, wound or whatever condition your horse is suffering from. However, having a good, broad-based knowledge of the subject is going to go a long way towards helping you make that decision.

Where essential oils alone are concerned, there are many publications on the market. It would be hard to pick a suitable book if you know nothing of the subject. I have chosen a few, which I can highly recommend as they are simple, informative and packed with knowledge and facts. Hand in hand with that is a recommendation of books about horses. It never ceases to amaze me how very little horse owners actually know about the animal species they own and profess to love. I have, therefore, also recommended a handful of books which will help you understand the horse, how it works, why, and the best way of dealing with it. It is all very well gleaning a vast knowledge about essential oils – but if you know nothing of the horse, frankly there is very little point in trying to apply your essential oil knowledge to it!

THE ILLUSTRATED ENCYCLOPAEDIA OF ESSENTIAL OILS
Author: Julia Lawless   *Publisher:* Element, Shaftesbury, Dorset
ISBN: 1-85230-721-8

I cannot praise this book highly enough and no bookshelf should be without it. It is beautifully illustrated, the layout is by far the best I have seen and the content is very comprehensive and easily understandable. It is not one of those books that tend to get too technical. This one tells it just as it is. If you were to have any reference book at all, then it should be this one. I promise you the pages will be well thumbed within a month of its purchase!

The number of oils it covers is the greatest I have come across in one book. Many of them are not needed or much used in every day oil usage. However, the broader your base of knowledge the better, and I have to say that there have been times when one of the more obscure oils has been the one that will bring a puzzling situation to its conclusion.

THE FRAGRANT PHARMACY
Author: Valerie Ann Worwood   *Publisher:* Bantam Press
ISBN: 0-553-40397-4

This book is based purely on oil use for humans. However, with care and understanding, there are some mixes that can be adapted for use on horses.

There are no pictures in this small but thick paperback, and therefore at first glance it might seem far too technical – however, experience is a wonderful thing. Learning to use oils on humans first is a good grounding for eventually using them on animals. It is not what I would call a cheap book but eminently suitable for those of you who would like to experiment a bit with essential oils.

AROMATHERAPY FOR HORSES
Author: Caroline Ingraham
Publisher: Threshold Picture Guides/USA – Half Halt Press
ISBN: 1-872082-98-X

This book is one of those small, glossy, square picture guides you see in most 'widget' sections of tack shops and saddlers. Being a picture guide, it is more informative in some areas than other publications. There are some really good blends in this book – which are easy for the first time user to make up and use. The drawback with this book is that it is too thin on information if you are new to essential oils and therefore it is not as broad-based as it might be. It is still a good book for beginners and will give you an idea of whether you want to use oils or not and what, in a general sense, it is all about. Despite its small size it is still one for the bookshelf.

AROMATHERAPY – AN A TO Z
Publisher: C.W. Daniel & Co., Essex.
ISBN: 0-85207-295-3

I like this book very much and refer to it often in my work with humans and essential oils. It covers almost everything and is easy to use – just look up the appropriate letter of the alphabet for whatever it is you want to know and you will find as full an explanation as you could want. A very helpful book for those new to essential oil usage.

AROMATHERAPY – THERAPY BASICS
Author: Helen McGuinness *Publisher:* Hodder & Stoughton
ISBN: 0-340-67993-X

I actually trained under Helen McGuinness and found all her teaching methods to be straightforward and easily understood. I bought this book months before I enrolled at her private college and found it to be invaluable. The book is set out in step-by-step chapters with a test section at the end of each chapter. The book formed the basis of the course we did with Helen.

I found that by using this book before going on the course I was so much better informed and had taught myself a lot just by using her test sections. It is surprising just how much you learn from doing this.

This book, coupled with the *Illustrated Encyclopaedia of Essential Oils*, would be all that most people need.

AROMATHERAPY TODAY
The international aromatherapy journal

This is a quarterly journal simply packed with information from around the globe, covering a vast array of subjects, books and oils and listing numerous suppliers around the world as well as in the UK.

It is informative, and although aimed at qualified therapists, is still comprehensible for lay people.

It can be obtained in the UK via Charles Wells, PO Box 126, Chipping Norton DO OX7 6GT. Tel: 01608 659933. In the USA, try the website www.aromatherapytoday.com.

VETERINARY NOTES FOR HORSE OWNERS
Author: Captain M. Horace Hayes FRCVS
(New edition edited by Peter D. Rossdale PhD., FRCVS)
Publisher: Ebury Press/USA – Simon & Schuster
ISBN: 0-09-171511-3

I simply would not be without this book. I dip in and out of it all the time. It is essential ownership for all those who have horses and are responsible for their day-to-day care. It is a weighty tome and does not come cheaply – in fact, you can buy a rug for the price of this book. But, what price knowledge? It covers absolutely every eventuality regarding the horse's health. Most important, it also answers the question of why something is the way it is, or happens the way it does. Buy it!

SHIATSU THERAPY FOR HORSES
Author: Pamela Hannay
Publisher: J.A. Allen & Co./USA – Trafalgar Square
ISBN:0-85131-847-9

This book is a new edition of one of my favourites (my own copy is showing distinct signs of wear and tear!). The book deals with equine behaviour and the use of shiatsu, a system of healing and health through touch. I have completed a Level I Shiatsu course and highly recommend it.

I met the late author, Pamela Hannay, and found her knowledge of horses to be infinite. She was also possibly the most serene person I have ever met.

Many of the massage or touching movements used have a good deal of their basis in shiatsu. This book shows all the movements in easy-to-follow picture form. I highly recommend this for your bookshelf.

INSIDE YOUR HORSE'S MIND
Author: Lesley Skipper   *Publisher:* J.A. Allen/USA – Trafalgar Square
ISBN: 0-85131-738-3

This, again, is not a book about essential oils. It is, however, a book about horses, and a challenging one at that. It is not for the faint-hearted but more for those serious about the subject of horses. It challenges many of the prejudices that have been built into our understanding of the horse. Based on the knowledge I gleaned from reading this book, I approached some situations slightly differently, and altered the type of oils I used.

It is not bedtime reading and certainly will not be read in a week or so. Be prepared to read this over a period of two months, say, to allow the information to filter through and be understood. If you are serious about learning and understanding equine behaviour, then this book should be read from cover to cover.

I have to say that the first chapter or two take some getting into, but once past those, the book seems to find its own groove and is an easier read.

AROMATHERAPY
The complete guide to essential oils

This is another quarterly journal, which I think once again is aimed more at the qualified therapist. However, it does give a huge amount of information about essential oils, what is currently in favour for what, where to get it, oil profiles, treatment profiles, guest articles and product information which is slanted more to the 'goodies' side rather than the professional. It is a nice magazine to have by the bedside or to take on a journey.

The more you know about everything to do with essential oil therapy, the more you will understand whether it is suitable for you or not.

This journal is distributed by Comag, Tavistock Road, West Drayton, Middlesex UB7 7QE. Tel: 01895 444055, or contact Aromatherapy Magazine, 53–79 Highgate Rd, London. They are due to go on-line during the middle of 2002.

CHAPTER 14

Suppliers of Essential Oils and Useful Holistic Websites

One of the points I have stressed in earlier chapters is that it is very important to find the very best suppliers of essential oils that you can. It can be very hard when starting out to know exactly where to find these companies and, even if you do, what they or their products are like. I am recommending companies that specialise in the production and sale of essential oils as they are the purest source of both information and product. Whilst there is nothing technically wrong in buying from high street outlets – and there are so many places selling essential oils, from garden centres to new age gift shops right through to supermarkets – it is still better to go to the supplier. The staff at these companies are trained to know about the product they are selling – very often this is not the case when buying from a retail outlet in the local town. There is also the safeguard of knowing how old the oil is, and that it will be despatched to you quickly and efficiently, usually by specialist carrier. The storage conditions of retail outlets are, for the most part, unknown. That is not to say that you could not buy an oil in an emergency from a retail outlet. I have done it often enough myself when an oil is needed instantly and have had no problems with it whatsoever. In the main, however, I have to recommend using suppliers direct, simply to ensure the highest quality product purchase. The advice that these companies provide is also invaluable.

PURPLE FLAME AROMATHERAPY
St. John's Spinney, Gun Hill, New Arley,
Warwickshire CV7 8WW
Tel: 01676 542542
www.purpleflame.co.uk

This company, as well as being a major supplier, also offers a wide variety of training courses.

Their oil list is as comprehensive as you could wish for, besides which they supply the most wonderful laminated wall charts. I am very fond of their Lavender oils. They have a healthy book list to choose from, together with all the items associated with aromatherapy, such as base lotions, creams, shampoos, conditioners, bubble baths and oils, containers of every description and also clays. This company offers a free customer aromatherapy help line, has computer software available and is generally about as good as it gets.

The staff manning the phone lines are always helpful polite and cheerful. Their mail order is good, fast and efficient and they offer a 10 per cent discount on your first order. Highly recommended.

THE HOLISTIC TRAINING CENTRE
1 Springfield Crescent, Portswood, Southampton,
Hants S017 2FD.
Tel: 023 80 390982
www.holistictrainingcentre.co.uk

This establishment is run by Helen McGuinness who also wrote one of the books on the recommended list in the previous chapter. The Holistic Training Centre is small and only takes about 10-12 students per course. Due to the small numbers the tuition is very much geared to an individual level and each student is encouraged to work on every other student, giving a very friendly, relaxed atmosphere. I did my own training here and can highly recommend it.

Helen also does a very comprehensive range of oils and associated products, which are bottled specifically for her. I particularly liked their Patchouli. The business is run very much on a hands-on basis by Helen and her husband Mark, giving a very personalised and approachable aspect to training courses there. Helen also does a lot of work in hospitals and with the elderly.

The website is accessible, easy to understand, and you can see everything at a glance.

ESSENTIALLY OILS LIMITED
8-10 Mount Farm, Junction Road, Churchill,
Chipping Norton, Oxon, OX7 6NP
Tel: 01608 659544
e.mail: sales@essentiallyoils.com

Everyone has their favourite company – and this is mine. I do use other suppliers from time to time but always find myself back at this one. They are a very knowledgeable bunch and are happy to impart that knowledge. Their oils, too, are just by far the ones I have the most success with. I like them more than other oils I buy – for reasons I am simply unable to explain! They just are very, very good. Their Chamomiles, for example, are just superlative. They send everything by special courier, which will be taken back if there is no one at home to receive the parcel. It is possible to issue instructions to Essentially Oils as to where the parcel can be left and these instructions are passed on to the couriers. Otherwise, if, like me, you are rarely at home during delivery hours, it is almost impossible to receive the parcel!

They do a vast range of bottles, jars, containers, base products and hydrosols (and I prefer theirs to any others I have bought; they are simply wonderful).

The one thing that I love about this company, though, is their monthly newsletter written by the redoubtable Charles. Charles is a dying breed and if ever you get the chance to talk oils with him, I highly recommend it. He has been everywhere, seen everything and done it too. His well of knowledge is therefore vast, and I would simply love to know just what he has forgotten! A true character. The newsletter brings information of new oils out, of new safety data, and a thorough history of the oil being 'targeted' that month. Hence I found out about Blue Tansy from America which is a wonderful mucolytic. Each month there is a list of special offers and at Christmas there are all sorts of goodies on the back page that are wonderful stocking fillers.

Very hard to beat this one!

NEW HORIZON AROMATICS
Horizon House, 44 Queensway, Southampton, Hants
SO14 3GT.
Tel: 023 80 399664
e.mail: nharoma@interalpha.co.uk

This is a small company, but with a good list of oils all of very high quality. I particularly like their bottles, which come in blue, amber and green.

Blue and green being my corporate colours, so to speak, I obviously find that very useful and very apt!

Their mail order is fast and efficient.

They have a selection of the more unusual items and it is well worth asking for one of their catalogues. I have visited their premises, which are tiny, but if you do not see what you want, ask. Invariably they produce it from the storage area.

In the back pages of the periodicals I recommended in the previous chapter, there are simply pages of suppliers of essential oils and associated products. I have recommended those above simply because I have used their products, had dealings with their staff and am therefore able to speak on a personal basis about them. I am sure there are many companies out there offering as good a service as those recommended here. The point being made here is that if, like many people reading this, you have never dealt with any of them, it is always helpful to have first hand guidance.

One point I meant to mention is that most companies offer a testing strip of any oil you wish to try. This is a small, very thin strip of paper that has been dipped in the oil at one end and it gives you an idea of what the oil is like before you purchase. This is an especially useful tool when trying to decide between, say, three or four different Lavenders or Chamomiles or Tea Tree. I have never yet paid for these, although I do not doubt the day will come when a nominal charge has to be levied.

One of the things I am most often asked is 'How do I find out about ….?'. Very often people we know want to try to use complementary methods on their horses, and would like to find out more information – but where should one look? Apart from the list of books and publications above, there is now the internet. Websites deal with everything under the sun – and horses are no exception. I have a website of my own and below are a few that I would recommend you 'visiting'.

www.equine-online.net

This is an equestrian site based on information shared, donated articles, advice on nutrition, horsemanship, horse and stable management and veterinary first aid.

www.taranet.co.uk

Apart from equestrian website design and advertising, it has an equine therapy directory covering acupuncture, chiropractic, equine massage, herbal remedies, homoeopathy, magnotherapy, physiotherapy, radionics, reiki and shiatsu.

Whatever your choice of complementary therapy, there seems to be someone who can give you information via this site. Well worth a visit.

www.spequine.com

This USA site has an on-line consultation facility, an anatomy discussion section, and a 'case of the month'.

www.equine-essential-oils.com

This is my own website with information on essential oil usage, kinesiology and products that can be purchased.

www.wingedseed.com

An all singing all dancing USA site that has everything to do with oils: accessories, base products, flower remedies, information on aromatherapy, classes, events, books etc. Well worth a look.

www.a-better-way.com

One of the few companies I could find that sell aloe vera gel.

www.namasteproducts.com

I loved this USA site. It had everything – oils, bottles, accessories, unscented bases, kits, baskets, giftbags, boxes and sets, with good explanations of the products and what was in them. The staff are approachable, informative and extremely helpful.

www.fragrant.demon.co.uk/us aromas.html

A useful listings site including USA suppliers and practioners.

CHAPTER 15

Photo Journal

An Instructional and Informative Guide to Some Essential Oil Practices

---

There are some things in life that are better seen rather than just written about and various aspects of essential oil usage would be better served by the visual rather than textual element. In the same way that a recipe book shows a picture of how the finished product should look, and perhaps how it should look along the way, so this selection of photographs will, I hope, be able to assist you.

Photo 15.1

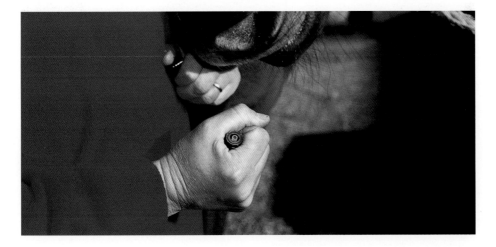

Photo 15.1 shows how you should hold the bottle containing the oils. As you can see, it is well down in the fist with just the top showing – note the insert in the

neck of the bottle. The reason for holding the bottle down in the fist is so that, from a safety point of view, the horse is not able to lift it out of your hand with its teeth. As you can see the nostril has already come over the top of the bottle and is flaring nicely – a good inhalation of oil particles is being experienced here.

Photo 15.2

Photo 15.2 shows how not to do it. The neck of the bottle is protruding too far above the closed fist. The horse is able to take this quite easily in its teeth, as the picture clearly shows. There is an accident waiting to happen if you offer the bottle in this way. Whilst the bottles are strong, the sheer force of the horse's teeth around the bottle is enough to shatter it. The consequences do not bear thinking about.

Photo 15.3

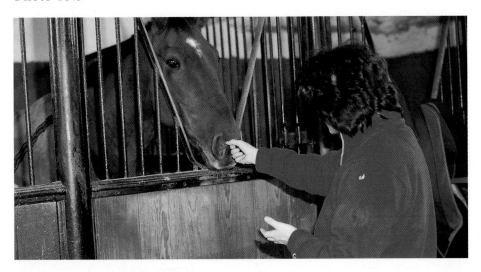

You can see the reaction of the horse to the smell of the oils. The ears are pricked forward, the eyes are bright and soft, the left nostril is dilating quite openly on the outer edge. I am perhaps a little too far back, and one step further forward would have been better.

Photo 15.4

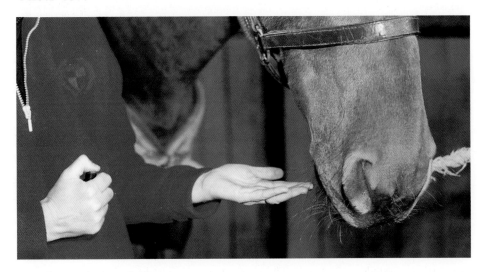

There are times when horses, a naturally suspicious species, are wary of a bottle. In that instance, let one or two drops of the oil fall into your palm and offer your palm

to the horse instead. As you can see in photo 15.4, the nostril has come around to my hand and is already beginning to dilate. The horse may want to lick this small amount from your hand and, providing it does not contain Eucalyptus, this is fine.

Photo 15.5

When horses detect a new smell they perform what is known as a Flehmen reaction. In this movement they curl their muzzle back against the nostrils, trapping the smell there and forcing it back into the nasal cavity. Here it is detected by the smell receptor cells located in the soft tissue under the blaze. It is very common to see a stallion do this when a new mare is introduced into a yard, or if a mare is in season. Here, the smell of Peppermint diluted in Almond oil has had the desired effect!

Photo 15.6

Barney has a close encounter with Peppermint. A small amount, diluted in Sweet Almond oil, has attracted him. Note how the ears are forward, the nostrils flaring, but the eyes are watchful and his stance is such that his near fore is ready to propel him away from this new experience.

Photo 15.7

In photo 15.7 Just Dougal, my daughter's pony, is simply not sure about this. He would not come any nearer even though he really did want to. The ears reflect his interest in that they are forward, but his eyes are deeply suspicious and he is allowing his nose to come within the minimum possible distance to allow him to detect the aroma. He licked his lips after this shot, but then backed off and would not come near again. It is important to respect this and not force any oil on a horse that does not want it.

Photo 15.8

There are many different containers that can be used to store essential oils. Photo 15.8 shows a selection that I use. The cantilevered metal carrier is useful because it keeps all the oils upright. Due to the sectioning at the bottom I could group my oils for ease of reference. For example, I had all the Citrus and top note oils in one section. The heavier base note oils, such as Vetiver and Violet Leaf, were kept in another section.

The flat briefcase-type carriers are fine, but you do need a heavy towel or a piece of foam to sit on top of the bottles and fit snug to the top of the case. This prevents the bottles from falling about whilst you are travelling. All these cases come in various sizes and are big enough to allow me to carry bottles, jars, tubs and carrier oils and gels.

All of these metal carriers were purchased from DIY outlets at a fraction of the cost of retail outlets that sold camera cases which are similar to those shown.

Wooden boxes for oils I have found to be prohibitively expensive. If you are going to have just six oils, then a small wooden box, such as that shown in the top right corner of photo 15.8, is fine. However the price of a wooden box to carry 36 oils will be excessive and as I convert all things to equine-related expenditure, I would rather buy a rug for the price of a wooden box! The metal carrying cases are a much cheaper alternative.

I am a firm believer in children being involved with their ponies as much as they can. The relationship they form with their pony will dictate how they perform together. Children should also learn to be aware that their pony is not a piece of machinery, but a living, breathing, being. I believe all children should be taught how to do flat hand exploration on their ponies *every day* if they are at home and handling them. It teaches them to read their ponies and to think of them as something other than a piece of sports equipment!

I have taught my 11-year-old daughter to do the flat hand exploration, (photo 15.9) and she is now beginning to notice where Dougal has rubbed himself raw, or has been kicked or bitten. She is beginning to learn where he feels stiff or hot or has cold spots.

Photo 15.9

Some of the easier stretches can also be performed by children. Photo 15.10 shows Olivia performing a leg bend that stretches the front of the leg, and also, from that position, the rotation of the fetlock joint.

Photos 15.10

Photo 15.11

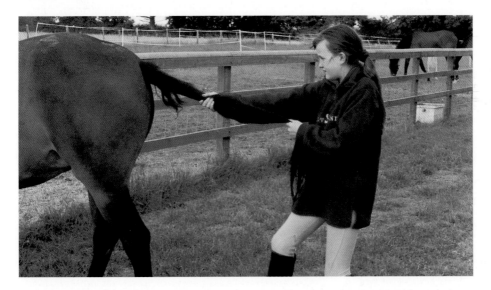

In photo 15.11 Olivia is doing the full tail stretch. Her position is quite good for a beginner!

This has also taught her to be more aware around the hind quarters of a horse and to read its body language To be aware is to be a better horsewoman.

Children on the whole, react well to being given responsibility. Under guidance,

209

I wholly advocate the little people, as they are known here, learning as much as the big ones!

Horses benefit tremendously from being touched because they are tactile animals. The hands on horses section will benefit them enormously. However, to be able to do the movements to the best of your ability you need to be supple and relaxed yourself. There is very little point in beginning a routine if you are tight and muscle cramped yourself. If you have just spent the day in the office hunched over a computer, you will bring very little benefit to your horse if you start a hands-on session before limbering up yourself. Hands are important; they are your instruments. Before commencing a massage session, shake them free of static, loosen the wrists by loose shaking them, turn your hands in circles from the wrist only, first one way and then the other. Flick your fingers free of static picked up from electrical equipment. Jewellery harbours static electricity and energy, especially crystals. If you are wearing jewellery, take it off before touching your horse. I promise you that, sometimes, to your horse, you will resemble a walking force field of energy. Therefore, should your horse back away from you at the end of a working day, this is probably why!

The photo sequence opposite shows a few exercises that will stretch you and release you. They will take no more than five minutes.

Start by holding your arms outstretched with your palms facing away from you. Lock fingers and push and stretch. The stretch should be felt across the upper back across the shoulder blades. Hold for a count of four and release (photo 15.12).

Reverse the exercise by pushing your arms out behind you, palms facing outwards, fingers interlocked. Push and stretch. Your chest should be pushed forward by the movement and you should feel it opening and stretching (photo 15.13).

Place one arm across your chest and, with the other in a bent position behind the elbow, bring the bent arm towards you. You should feel the stretch through the shoulder and upper arm. Hold for a count of four and then release. Repeat with the other arm (photo 15.14).

Place one hand behind your head, reaching down for the opposite shoulder blade. Place your free hand on the elbow and push the arm downwards. You should feel the stretch in the back of the upper arm and through the upper shoulder area. Hold for a count of four and repeat with the other arm (photo 15.15).

Photo 15.12

Photo 15.13

Photo 15.14

Photo 15.15

Photo 15.16 Photo 15.17

Side stretches will release your torso and help ease the oblique muscles around the waist area. Stand with legs apart. Slide one hand down the leg to just below the knee, bringing the other arm over your head pushing as you go. You will feel a release in the muscles around your waist on that side and through the shoulder. Hold for a count of four and repeat on the other side (photo 15.16).

*Hamstring stretch. Place one leg slightly forward of the other and loose bent at the knee. Place the other leg straight out behind you. Your hands should be on your waist. Now lean forward into the soft bend of the knee. You should feel **everything** stretch down through the calf and the thigh. Most of you will groan, of that I have no doubt! Hold for a count of four and repeat on the other leg (photo 15.17).*

Photo 15.18

The front leg stretch is equally important. Lean forward, with one leg slightly in front of the other, with the toes pointing upwards. The rear leg should be bent and soft at the knee. Place your hands one over the other on the thigh of the forward leg. Bend forward slowly and feel the leg stretch! (photo 15.18)

Now you will be ready to put your hands on horses!

Finally, taking a quiet moment with your horse after a body session is a nice way to round off the hands on session. In fact, taking a quiet moment with your horse, even if you do not have time to ride or do a massage session, is therapy itself. Pour a little bit of carrier containing a few drops of Lavender or Jasmine into the palm of your hand, and spread this down the neck and then just both stand and inhale the aroma. After a hands-on session, most horses are feeling very mellow. They appreciate time, and it is such a small thing to give and enhances your relationship to beyond that of just horse and rider.

Photo 15.19

CHAPTER 16

Tail Ends

The subject of essential oils is not a new one but the subject of essential oils in relation to horses is. Therefore, as a subject in its infancy, there are no hard and fast rules. It is all still one huge learning curve. It does not matter what I or others like me achieve in this field, there will always be people who know how to do it better, faster, deeper or more effectively. There will always be people who say, '*I* don't do it *that* way, I do it *this* way'. And so they might. The differences are just that – differences – and not a barometer of what is either right or wrong.

It has to be remembered that a blend of oils used by one person for a certain ailment may well be dismissed by someone else in favour of another blend. What works for one horse may not work for another. Essential oils are idiosyncratic and nothing is ever going to change that. It is also why training in essential oils is so necessary if you are to apply those oils to either humans or animals. It is that very understanding of the idiosyncratic nature of the medium that you are dealing with which could make the difference between a successful application of oils and one that becomes a problem. It is never going to be possible to say that an oil *will* achieve the results A, B or C. On another horse it may achieve only A and C, but also D as well.

As each oil is different, so is the human or animal it is being applied to. Each horse has a different temperament and different personality and requires a different approach. Horses are not robots or machines. They are living, breathing, thinking, sometimes reasoning beings, in the same way as a human is a living, breathing, thinking, sometimes reasoning being. We have many attributes that are the same, but we are all still different from each other. Horses do not have a set way of reacting to things, any more than humans do. Therefore it is important to remember not to be put off by the amount of differences you will surely encounter within this sphere – but simply to see them all as learning experiences.

One point I must stress again, so that it is in your mind as you finish this book, is that essential oils are **not** a cure-all. If there is a problem with your horse, you need a vet, the same as you would always do. Essential oils are not a replacement or alternative to conventional medicine but a complementary side to it. Why they sometimes work when all else from a vet, say, has failed, is because a vet tends to approach a problem in isolation and on the symptoms prevailing at the time. This is what they have been trained to do. A holistic practitioner, however, tends to treat the being as a whole – which is what *they* have been trained to do. It is a difference you are unlikely to reconcile for many generations.

I am always explaining to people who telephone with a problem and say 'My horse has a lump on its back, what can you do for it?'– that I am not at the head of the list of people that they should be phoning. I come somewhere towards the end of it – after the vet, the farrier, the saddler and the chiropractor! It seems a hard concept for people to take in when they wish to avail themselves of 'other' practices for their horse and I push them back in the direction they are heading away from.

I cannot stress strongly enough the need to understand the difference between the words 'alternative' and 'complementary'. Many think they are one and the same. They are not. Alternative means something else, another choice or way of doing things. Complementary means to complement something that exists already, a way of enhancing and making that which exists work more efficiently. It should always be remembered that it is against the law to knowingly withhold treatment from an animal and cause it to suffer – so do not neglect to call a vet because you feel a holistic treatment will be better for your horse. It might well be, but usually on the advice of a qualified vet.

It is important that your vet is aware of what has been used upon a horse, in the event that the horse has an adverse reaction, or even just to learn that something else exists that works on the problem presenting itself. There are times when all normal avenues have been exhausted – and this is the point where a complementary therapy comes into its own and has a chance to shine. I obviously do long for the day when all veterinary practices have their own holistic practitioner on the premises. Pigs might grow wings, some might say. Quite so. However, I do know someone who once saw an elephant fly – so perhaps it is not an utterly impossible dream after all!

Hopefully, by now, if you have read this book from cover to cover, section by section, you should have a broad-based knowledge of the world of essential oils and how they connect with horses. From this, perhaps, you can work and grow. Some of you may wish to go into one of the holistic professions and work with horses yourselves; some of you may be vets who now hold a more enlightened view on the matter. Some of you will push it aside and mutter about it being complete rubbish and use the book as a mat to put your coffee cups on! But then there will be those of you for whom it has switched on a light, who will buy books, research more, perhaps train in essential oils or one of the other complementary therapies – and horses will eventually benefit. If that is so, then it will have been well worth writing this book.

As for essential oils, I just do not think that you can ever know enough. There is always something more to learn, something new being discovered all the time. This guidebook is the tip of a very big iceberg indeed.

Carole Faith

Bibliography

Flower Power, Anne McIntyre, Henry Holt & Co., New York, 1996

Practical Aromatherapy, Shirley Price, Thorsons (HarperCollins), 1994

Aromatherapy Workbook, Shirley Price, Thorsons (HarperCollins), 1993

Aromatherapy an A to Z, Patricia Davis, The C.W. Daniel Co. Ltd., 1995

Aromatherapy, Chrissie Wildwood, Bloomsbury Publishing Plc., 1997

The Fragrant Pharmacy, Valerie Ann Worwood, Bantam Books, 1997

Healing with Essential Oils, Nicola Naylor, Gill & Macmillan Ltd, Dublin, 1997

Aromatherapy – A Guide for Home Use, Christine Westwood, Amberwood Publishing Ltd., 1991

Aromatherapy – Therapy Basics, Helen McGuinness, Hodder & Stoughton, 1997

Aromatherapy, Judith Jackson, Dorling Kindersley, 1993

Essential Oil Safety, Robert Tisserand/Tony Balacs, Churchill Livingstone, 1998

Veterinary Aromatherapy, Nelly Grosjean, The C.W. Daniel Co. Ltd., 1996

The Illustrated Encyclopaedia of Essential Oils, Julia Lawless, Element Books Ltd., 1997

Encyclopaedia Brittanica

The Collins Concise English Dictionary

Acknowledgements

An author does not write a book alone. Many unseen hands facilitate its creation. I would like to thank all those of you who have made this book possible.

The late Pamela Hannay for showing me the serenity of another way – she will be much missed. Caroline Burt of J.A. Allen simply for believing in it and for giving me more time – a precious gift indeed!

Gerry for helping me whisper to horses and find out if I was hitting targets at all.

Anne Gray for taking on my share of the burden of looking after horses when I took to my computer and refused to leave it.

Colin and Feen Tett, and their wonderful stable of horses, for allowing me to use them as guinea pigs for the photoshoot and all their premises when mine were knee deep in mud.

Ben Crozier for tolerating my instant demand for printing colour copies and whatever else I pleaded that I needed yesterday if not sooner.

Daniel, my stepson, for simply being there and sorting out my computer gaffes twenty times a day, and 'retrieving' the book when I had consigned it to a dark and distant place by one press of a button, and for doing all those school runs – I am eternally grateful!

To all the horses, who stood patiently whilst I faffed around them with strange-smelling things and came up trumps. They are the stars of the show.

Olivia my daughter, for putting up with a part-time mother for the last year and for posing for photographs and being shouted at for her trouble, because she was not *exactly* how I wanted her.

Karin and Russell who allowed me to take over their dining room table in the serenity of the Emerald Isle and who fed and watered me without uttering a word so that I could catch up on lost time!

Melissa and Tracey for posing for my photographs.

Len Beach, my vet, for believing in me.

A big thank you to Jon Stone, the photographer. He was patience itself when I was not the easiest person to deal with by any means!

Finally, my husband John who, with grace and equanimity, came to accept my absence and the fact that food was not always an option in the house during the writing of this book. I thank you for your tolerance.

Index